Best wishes

THE ANIMAL FAIR

THE
ANIMAL
FAIR

Thad Stem, Jr.

McNally of Charlotte / 1960

This book is for my girl friends—
For Sallie Hamilton Tarry, who is three,
And for Dety and Bernice Kelly Harris,
Who are a little older.

Contents

Sis Goose and Cudin Flying Squirrel

This is an account of the inordinate admiration of Sis Goose for her cudin, a noble flying squirrel. "Cudin," as Professor H. W. Fowler must have known, is the word high-born Southerners used when they were saying "cousin."

All this happened a number of years ago when the ratio of barnyard animals was considerably larger. In those gregarious days, barnyard animals had such distinctive personalities some of them would have been photographed for the Easter Parade, most likely, if the rotogravure process had then been perfected.

Sis Goose lived in one of the Virginias, and as I seem to recall my early history reading, it was not in West Virginia. Sis Goose was not a bad bird at all. She did her normal household tasks adequately but without any real inspiration. She laid her quota of goose eggs regularly but this was accomplished without boasting or any visible display of genuine concern. She did her job but it was always a perfunctory performance, devoid of verve and aplomb. In brief, Sis Goose was methodically competent but generally wanting in exuberance.

For instance, the wild geese passed by her bailiwick going from Canada to the southern marshlands. When this migration occurred, the other barnyard citizens mounted a pleasant knoll to watch the flying geese, or to be undiplomatically graphic, to laugh at the "screaming hobos" as so many barnyarders alluded to the northern tourists. During all the observation and the derision, Sis Goose hardly looked up, although everyone knew

1

she was almost bound to have some distant relatives somewhere in this aerial circus. It wasn't that Sis Goose was disdainful of the frenetic transients so much as she was passively indifferent to the stranger that passed above with all the impotent fury of a windmill beating his arms vigorously.

The only comment Sis Goose ever made (and this was made one time when exasperation was augmented by a touch of indigestion) was this: Canada must be a dismal place or these screaming hobos were as bereft of patriotism and community ties and responsibilities as a Portuguese dollar in a dockside crap game at Newport News.

But hardly anything ever interested her, aside from Cudin Flying Squirrel. Even the annual ritual of hog-killing neither whetted her gastric juices nor elicited one slow tear of commiseration.

Sis Goose apparently lived only to watch Cudin Flying Squirrel, to sit enthralled as he performed incredible feats of graceful daring. The other barnyarders pooh-poohed this dubious kinship. But Sis Goose smiled the way a saint smiles when pestered by officious children. If Cudin Flying Squirrel was not a kissing cudin, the fault lay in distance and in an unbalance of agility. It was not Sis Goose's fault. Nor could the blame be ascribed to any remote lack of hero-worship.

When the weather was light and fair, Sis Goose took her leisure in a luscious grove. The birds might sing as if song would vanish from the earth in the next five minutes. The leaves might dance until the world was blind to all save greenery. The brook might babble in a dozen tongues simultaneously. The blue clouds might play a game of "Going to Jerusalem." But Sis Goose was adamant to these charms. She sat stolidly until Cudin Flying Squirrel came to the wondrous grove.

Often Cudin Flying Squirrel kept Sis Goose waiting for an hour, or more. The barnyarders said he did this to get up her dander. However, the most discerning could detect no apprehension or impatience in Sis Goose's placid features. For, what if an ugly rain cloud appeared momentarily? Cudin Flying Squirrel would come cavorting, ere long, and the sky would be a fairyland, an actual paradise visible to the naked eye.

Cudin Flying Squirrel bounced from limb to limb, from tree to tree, when he was of the notion. He danced on the luxuriant grass below the majestic trees, performing now an exquisite ballet, then a stunning arabesque, or next a sprightly reel with himself taking all the parts. And Sis Goose beamed her sublime happiness and approval the delicately wondrous way Mrs. Browning smiled her cherub's smile when the critics were kind to her Robert.

No untoward intervention beclouded this immaculate rapport. Oh, the gray hen might come running to say a hawk had lost his balance and broken his evil neck. Ah, the gamboling lamb might even offer his miraculous wool for a pallet.

Mayhap, the rabbit came frolicking to tell how he'd caught a very naughty boy in a box, but nothing marred the pristine communion between Sis Goose and Cudin Flying Squirrel.

You see (if this message isn't getting across), Sis Goose was in a barnyard class all by herself. Supremely diffident, she deigned not to turn her head if the rooster sang impassioned trains from "Le Coq d'Or" while the hen caught grubbing worms big enough to choke a channel bass. The goat might come back from his foraging with every tin can in the commonwealth, but Sis Goose neither pecked nor spun around.

When the other animals made sport of Sis Goose, as envious and jealous creatures are wont to do, she demurred not, not even by way of aloof parenthesis. When the petty critics

pointed out that squirrels and geese are not of a feather, that
Sis Goose could never be a flyer in a circus, she gently turned
to her Browning and said: "Ah, that one's reach should exceed
his grasp, or what's heaven for?"

Oh, they accused her of being too big for her tail feathers,
of trying to go beyond her raising. Some even pointed the error
in her mushmelon pronunciation. The duck was brash enough
to suggest that geese in the best finishing schools and homes long
ago abandoned "Cudin" for "cousin" so that Yankee Christians
would know what in the hell they are talking about.

But, Sis Goose turned her head ever so daintily and looked
to the distant hills as if each one were a forest inhabited solely
by billions of Cudin Flying Squirrels.

When the other denizens of coop, nest, roost, and matted
straw had their seasonal celebrations, Sis Goose stayed in the
luscious grove. The May Court to her was less than naught. The
Harvest Ball was a picayune and all the Mid-Winter Frolics
were rowdy conclaves studded with Johnnys-come-lately. Sis
Goose concentrated on Cudin Flying Squirrel and when she
was on the nest, perforce, or the victim of inclement weather,
she pored over the untarnished legends of the chivalric squirrels of yore, beaming with buoyant pride when a nebulous cud-
inship was established with one of the lordly ghosts.

Then, one beastly day of doom, the earth quaked and roared
and the sky opened its wounded side for drainage. A Yankee
with a mean beard and an offensive cigar came with pen and
ink and butterfly net and seized Cudin Flying Squirrel in mid-
flight, just as the wizard was executing a marvelous triple-back-
somersault. This cigar-smoking Yankee clipped Cudin Flying
Squirrel's wings and stuffed him into a mighty tome called "A
Natural History of The United States."

For weeks and weeks Sis Goose languished in the verdant grove, too stunned to take nourishment or stock of the situation. Then the locusts came and for eleven long years they ruled the pleasant grove, which, by now, more nearly resembled a wooded hog pen.

But Sis Goose kept her lonely vigil with steadfast militance. By and by she came to realize that Cudin Flying Squirrel would never return, not in his corporeal estate. But, Sis Goose, faithful to the legend, steadfast to the faith, sat in the de-locusted grove telling the geeselets about Cudin Flying Squirrel, their very own cudin, and of the days when he walked the loam not as mortal squirrel but was so marvelously fashioned as to be less of earth than heaven.

Even to this holy hour, the geeselets gather in what is left of the luscious grove and they sing the song of haunting hope that Sis Goose left as her flaming testament so long ago: "Save your old pecan shells, geeselets, Cudin Flying Squirrel will leap again."

The Hunter's Moon

The Hunter's Moon comes when the early fall is a golden flower devouring itself by dint of its own passionate yearning. The Hunter's Moon usually comes early in October when the earth is tender as lips and breasts are tender, and the humming songs of the little rivers are sighs of desire to stay the winter and to call back the pageant of late spring.

The hills are honeycombed with many small fires where hunters sit calmly debating weather, crops, politics, and dogs.

The season for chasing possums, coons, and foxes commences officially when the fires sputter on the hills. This is the one remaining sport wherein thrill is not predicated on visible result. Men gather to hear hounds give mouth, to rediscover the smack and twang of the fall woodlands, to let the night air sweep the cobwebs from the brain and juice up the body with the old wines of elemental expectancy.

If a fox or a coon or a possum is caught, that's all to the good. But if the tub-thumping, baby-waking music of the chase leads to no specific accolade, no one is disappointed. Many folks attest to the succulence of cooked possum and coon, but a lot of the most rambunctious hunters say the meat is too greasy. Occasionally, fox hunting becomes a temporary crusade when the gray demons are said to be destroying crops. But taking it all in all, fox hunters have paid out far more cash for the inadvertent damage yelping hounds have done while tracking the prey than all the foxes ever destroyed in the way of crop foraging. The big thing about the fox menace, about impending agricultural disaster, is the hunter has an excuse to be away from home for six straight nights in a week.

The Hunter's Moon still has tremendous psychological implications. In the Southern States the crops are housed and already being sold. The incessant sweat and toil of the steaming summer hours are past. The time of the fruit of the harvest is at hand. It is a time to take a long look around. October spreads her multi-colored apron in the manner of a thoughtful grandmother bringing choice tidbits to her grateful flock. The respite of the ample time of fall is at hand.

Stories flow as easily as water from a spring. Almost every pseudo hunter knows an outlandish animal story. The night is conducive to mellow cordiality, and every yarnsmith has his say. The fire shine and the moonbeams are magic wands, and the stuff brought along in jars and bottles doesn't exactly stifle imaginative volubility. The contagion of the night and the inner music is highly infectious. Everyone is as happy as a blind man in a gallery of ultra, esoteric modern art.

So considerate and deferential is everyone, a stranger might assume this is a rustic meeting of garrulous and slightly profane Quakers. Refreshments are passed with the gentle flourishes with which ladies hand around tea cups, even if the ultimate effect is somewhat different. Everybody rakes a sweet potato from the ashes and leans back to listen to the stories. Faces are almost obscured by the tranquil haze that comes from pipes and cigarettes. Such courtly proceedings would hardly be equaled at a state dinner at the governor's mansion.

Hounds are off at a distance, all but forgotten. A live trail is struck with shattering suddenness. Hounds begin to give mouth. Everyone jumps up and gives mouth. It is as if these human voices are hounds' echoes. One man exclaims: "That's my Stella in the lead." Another butts in: "I beg your pardon, sir, but that's my Belle." A third scowls intensely and yells: "You are both damn liars. 'At ain't no bitch in the lead. It's my old Hickory Jim, just as show as God made little green apples."

Then someone else races around the fire furiously as an Apache around a settler at the stake. He whips his flanks with his hat, as if he were a horse. He bays, barks, and moans. He smiles as if he had swum all the way to shore from the Titanic: "All fox hunters are deaf as fish and crazy as bed-bugs. My little old Charmin' Billy's in the lead now, I God. You lying bastards couldn't hear thunder if you was on a black cloud."

Everybody grabs his own jug or bottle and puts his sweet potato in his jacket pocket.

Three hours later, when the last hound is caught, everyone is too tired to argue. Each hunter catches hounds indiscriminately and hands them over to the rightful owners. The next day there is muttering on the street. Some ominous scowls flash when hunters pass each other. But by dusky dark that night, everyone is greeting his buddy as if the two were the only humans who survived an H-bomb war. Hounds are put in the trailers and the car is loaded with happy hunters, the jugs, and the potatoes. From the manner in which they look at one another, you would think they are all going to heaven in the same automobile. The flowing essence of brotherly love permeates the woods. That is, that is until a fool hound strikes a fresh scent. That's how it is on those quixotic nights under the Hunter's Moon.

Caroline the Fox

Local historians disagree in trying to figure out wily Caroline's age. There are those who contend that she first showed the year the big oak tree fell in Frank Freeman's yard, while others hotly interpose: "No, no, man, you're 'way, 'way off. It was the year the Fuller boy turned over the hornets' nest in Little Zion Church." And still others tell how their grandpaps hunted Caroline as lads in short pants. And irascible old Squire Pettigrew argued until the day he died that Caroline broke up a rally for W. J. Bryan in the fall of '96.

Now, some of the oldest men will take you by the sleeve and mutter that Caroline really wasn't born of a fox at all. No, siree, her mammy was a gray cloud and her pappy was a whirlwind.

And the colored people know it to be an unimpeachable fact that Caroline was born during "Old Christmas," that she was whelped and nurtured by Old Christmas spirits that skinned the cat on a locust tree and then took refuge in an abandoned fox hole.

But all the way from Tally Ho Township, where Sweetgum Creek lies sunning in the brush like a silver worm, to Sassafras Fork Township, where Coon Creek rattles down the clay banks like a truant boy playing leap-frog, everyone knew that Caroline could vanish right smack before your very eyes. If she willed, she could become a rock in Coon Creek, or an elm tree along a ferny lane, or a hollow tree straddling a hole in a sunken field. She could turn herself into mist, or she could run over the hill and become a part of the dust that her flying heels kicked up. Her eyes were dark stars upon a winter night, and her sleek back was a rain-cloud.

The legends came and left like a trail of swamp smoke, but Caroline just went on and on and on. Puppies grew to hound-dom, got old and feeble and died. Each great one had his turn, and each one toppled before the will-o'-the-wisp. To name a few, there were Turkey Trot, winner of the All-Age and sire of Colonel Henry, the National Bench Champion, sire of Whangdoodle, that gave mouth as if the heavens were falling. Each in his day gave fervent chase to the drop of quicksilver, but on and on Caroline ran, exploding over the hill like wind-blown mist, majestic, supreme, eternally aloof and sublimely untouched.

The oldest men spat from the breeze and passionately vowed that Caroline could turn herself into a leaf when the chase was too hot. She'd turn herself into a leaf and hang onto the tree, frolicking in the breeze while hapless hounds passed by as forlornly as children lost in a maze of woodland tracks. I've heard reliable men say that Caroline once changed herself into a fish and lay up under the creek bank, sucking the cool moss, while hounds ran an absurd circle, menacing their own tails. And one of the Warren boys said he'd be damned and double-damned if the sun didn't lower a golden staircase for Caroline when she grew weary of entertaining irksome hounds.

Choleric old Squire Pettigrew died cursing a monstrous fate and Caroline, for it was the morning of the Township Hunt when the dark angel got him on a sight race and clipped his brush. The expiring squire finally upbraided the astonished clergyman who was reading prayers with: "Stop all that damned nonsense, man. Open the window, Nany. Open that window! Can't they catch that damned strumpet before I die! Listen. Listen. I'll vow they are right on top of her now! Listen! Oh, my God, listen! Of all the rotten, stinking luck—"

But even the Squire, if he had lived to continue his diatribe, would tell you that Caroline was the best damned nursemaid there ever was. Yes, sir. The Warren boys would start out with their pack of wondrous Walker hounds, as proudly as a troop of cavalry with banners and guidons streaming. At night they'd return as bedraggled as birds too tired to fly. But old Caroline always ended up the hunt through Gregory's Meadow so that spent hounds would be hard by the kennels, and the Warrens would not have to miss a night from the festivities of dancing by searching the countryside for lost hounds.

When a dry spell was as unending as farmer's hard-luck talk, and a scent harder to raise than cash in planting time, Caroline would wait under the black-gum bushes by the old railroad cut. This was a tacit agreement between Caroline and the Warrens, men and hounds. She would strut up and down in plain view until the pack came tumbling over the hillside with all the fury of unrequited love. First, she'd lead them down by the grist mill. Henry Tyler, the miller, was an old hunter whom time had winded. But this way he could see a chase and never leave his rocking chair; sit in the shade and see Caroline tear across the new ground like a gray chip blown crazily by a tornado.

Or, if the Warrens ran puppies, Caroline always high-balled down to the grassy places, obviously in deference to tender young puppy feet. Sometimes, just for the sport of the thing, she led them to the creek to watch cumbersome puppies floundering in the water as skittishly as ploughboys walking in tight, brand-new, store-bought brogans. But if the sun shone too brightly, you could bet your crop that Caroline would shoot like a meteor to Dewberry Springs and the sweet water that tasted like a chilled julep. But always, when the chase became precarious, she'd vanish like a candle flame before the storm. Where she went no man can any more tell than where the candle flame goes when the wind puts it out.

When the one-gallused Tulgins from Lickskillet Hollow ran their two-dollar potlickers by night, Caroline ran an easy circle. She kept hounds close to the fire, within short reach of the whiskey jug.

For the fancy, duded-up, blooded Trotters and their gaily bedecked horsemen, she sought the open fields where pink coats could bob along like red corks on a rolling green sea. Invariably she ended up the Trotter's hunt in front of the Big House, right when the supper bell was ringing. The old men say this gesture was not predicated alone upon Caroline's innate good manners and her impeccable consideration, but also upon a suppressed histrionic desire.

For when the gigantic raucous of horses, riders, hounds, hark-to-ers and Caroline came catapulting down the ferny lane, all the countryside turned out to witness the imminent kill. But then something always happened to people's eyesight. The dust got too thick, or the sun slanted the wrong way. Whatever it was, Caroline couldn't be seen. She'd disappear utterly, become a fence rail, or a cloud, or a hickory nut. And thwarted and exasperated hounds tucked their goofish tails and sauntered contritely to the pen. Thus it was that great ladies and grand gentlemen turned to brimming decanters to wash away the sting of this prodigious enigma.

And, best of all, oh, happy, happy day, she led the vociferous, vituperative, anti-social Branch boys right through the swamp, so that the damned scoundrels would have to expend much golden moonlight seeking hounds lost in brambles.

I'd clean forgotten about Whiskey Jones, the old Hard-shell preacher who always took his hounds to prayer meeting just in case. I can tell you there was more scrambling at Little Zion Church than there can possibly be at Chestnut Grove Cemetery on Judgment Day morning. There was a rail fence in front of the church that was known as the "merry-go-round." The Whiskey Jones' hounds were tied here. And no sooner would Whiskey Jones line out the first hymn than here'd come Caroline tearing around the sycamores like a sinner with brimstone scorching her tail.

Then such barking that one would think the moon had melted! Fence rails flew like flakes of snow. First, they'd be in Ransome's yard, over by the schoolhouse, and next going down the road lickity-split like a carryall drawn by four runaway horses. And then old Whiskey Jones'd come galloping from the meeting house as if Satan were prodding him with a pitchfork.

"Glory, hallelujah. Amen. Use all the doors, folks. Glory, hallelujah. Amen. Hark to her! Glory, hallelujah. Amen. Hark to her, Betsy! Har yar, Sambo. Glory, hallelujah. Amen. Brother Higgins, turn them other hounds a-loose."

"O, give me that old-time religion,
Hark to her, Betsy, har yar, Sambo!
T'was good fer Paul and Silas
And hit's good ernough fer me.
Glory, hallelujah. Amen. Amen.
Hark to her, I say."

Just when Whiskey Jones conjured exquisite visions of Caroline's tail flying above his dog pen, the ethereal will-o'-the-wisp would vanish like the sounds of a church bell, permeating the countryside with a mocking void. And he who could find the sounds of vanished church bells could unearth the habitat of Caroline.

So it went. Chasing Caroline was comparable to breaking down an oak tree with a jimson weed. It was like the farmer whose land is mostly rocks. He continues to chase after good times that he doesn't actually expect to apprehend. But the quest must go on. Men who hunted Caroline as beardless boys lay in the graveyards, and the scrub pines that once held in brittle fingers the music of the hunt were majestic woodlands.

But I am as prolix as the old men in their anecdotage who take forever and forever to get to the point. Some say it was the story of Sampson all over again; that a lousy coon dog bit off Caroline's tail and the ignominy of this made her die immediately of bitter shame. Others say, it being the second day of the celebration, that the Old Christmas spirits fetched her home again. Some of the incurable romantics say that Elijah lowered his golden chariot and personally escorted her to fox heaven.

But actually, and I know, Polycarp Warren found her the morning of the Township Hunt. She was lying there all curled up and warm on Squire Pettigrew's grave. And there wasn't a mark on her. No, siree, nor a hair out of place. But there was no Township Hunt that day. We buried her in a pink coat in the white folks' cemetery, right at Squire Pettigrew's feet. And there is a marker for all to see, and the tender legend is cast in metal. There's even a poem there; I know because I wrote it. And the Warren boys sent clean to Raleigh for an artist fellow to draw a picture of Caroline as we described her. This picture is in the court house for all to see, right under Senator Broadwhaite's portrait, right next to a cannon ball that didn't explode at Seven Pines.

That's about all there is to it, except that the one-gallused Tulgins from Lickskillet Hollow went back to coon hunting and making liquor and ended up in the county jail. And the Warren boys sold the wondrous Walker hounds to some rich Yankees and took to bird hunting. Whiskey Jones, until the day he died, never went to Little Zion Church again, and the meeting house is a brier patch and the clapper's gone from the bell.

But the colored people vow they've seen Old Christmas spirits skinning the cat in a locust tree and playing going-to-Jerusalem around a 'simmon tree. They'll all tell you that Caroline will come flying back one frosty morning, sailing like a gray cloud, flashing by like a bar of lightning. Just you wait and see!

The Pitiful Quail Hunter

In the eyes of small boys the quail hunter is a better man lying down than Paul Bunyan was standing on top of a ladder. And although this hunter's wife adores the wondrous white meat he fetches, she understands the process about as well as Henny Penny understood nuclear physics.

The quail hunter's Irish Setter is more blessedly resilient than the sound of a steam whistle was to Robert Fulton. However, to his wife, this four-legged epitome of courage and intelligence is poochie. She says poochie can't do anything. He has no tricks. So, she tries to get him to return a thrown stick. The hunter tries to explain that this action is more insulting than asking Thomas Hart Benton to do a mural for an outhouse.

In the field the hunter makes shots he believes would make Bill Cody look like a cross-eyed man with a home-made bow and arrow. The setter smells quail quicker than the Watch and Ward Society ever smelled incipient bedroom hanky-panky. This setter finds and retrieves so marvelously he makes the man who took the message to Garcia look like a boy scout on his first hike. After grueling but fruitful hours, man and noble beast return home laden with lustrous dinners.

The devoted wife asks: "Did you 'catch' anything, sweetie?" He holds up the quail, numbly. "Was poochie with you when you caught the doves?" He stares blankly. "Did you use that old gun you keep in the leather thing, or did you take that pistol you brought home from the war?"

He drops the gun so jerkily it almost goes off, and he feels pretty much as Sir Walter Raleigh felt a few minutes before he took his dose of "strong medicine" in the Tower of London.

The Bear Went over the Mountain

There used to be a song, a round, about the bear that went over the mountain to see what he could see. According to the song, the other side of the mountain was all that he could see. A lot of folks have assumed that disappointing trek was the last trip the bear made across the mountain. The bear, seeing more of the same, a repetition of the home precinct, lumbered back home to venture no more. That is not wholly true.

The bear went over the mountain once more, only recently. In lieu of whole ranges he saw more restaurants and hotels than there were spruce trees before the timber was cut, originally. He saw more gift stands and snack bars than an old-timey Pathe News cameraman could photograph. He even saw one of his nephews chained in front of a place where you could look through a telescope at an invisibly high peak, for fifty cents a look. He saw kids, as well as adults, paying two bits for the privilege of having their pictures taken standing beside his nephew on the chain.

The bear saw Indians, real live ones from the reservation, getting sick trying to learn to smoke peace pipes made in Japan. He saw these same Indians, dressed up in mail-order doeskin, trying to master the intricate arts of bows and arrows shipped in from New Jersey. And the bear heard a word never before spoken in all this vast wilderness. He heard Indians who have graduated from college trying to say "Ugh" for the edification of little white boys who wore pinwheels atop their summer caps.

The bear saw a million sacred shrines straight from the heart of local history, or certainly physical illusions made historic by decades of fervent wistfulness. At every shrine the bear saw some conductor or conductoress, garbed in period raiment, exuding a pat spiel more accurate than the one the medicine show man spoke but infinitely less poetic. And all these wonders, the bear could see and hear for a buck or so.

The bear threw up. The bear threw up, in monumental proportions. And the news along the creek is he still can't take solid nourishment.

Still, the Plowman

The catholic ramifications of spring plowing are subdued in the mass parade to urbanization. Land is still broken but this news is no longer a cannon fired to hail a monumental event. Spring plowing time used to be bell-tolling, fence-rattling celebration. People smiled because the eternal tryst between plow and earth was a signal that humanity's hopes were marshaled into a mighty attacking force.

Town and country were close together, close despite the impassable roads, the gigantic mudholes and the dust that covered highways thickly as snow storms. Spring plowing was a joint program. No matter what you did for a living, you were absorbed in the movement. Furrow and shop were side by side, despite the intervention of several ghastly, unpaved miles.

The general contagion of this smacking ebullience has long subsided, but the earth is still a brown-eyed boy whistling a tune, in plowing time. The earth is a well about to explode with fever. In the small towns some people still break land for vegetable gardens. Some plots are broken by tractor-plows, but the official town plowman, the old colored man, is yet in demand. This demand seems to be predicated more on a subconscious desire to perpetuate legend than on any utilitarian enhancements.

In the fresh vigor of early morning, you see the old man riding his ramshackle wagon, the plow in the wagon bed. This horse evidently was too old for military service in Washington's army, but he swings the rolling junk heap at a jaunty clip. A dog sits on the improvised board seat, by the plowman. (This is as inevitable everywhere as tassel on cornstalks.) The dog may be good for nothing more than putting his feet on the ground

17

and eating his head off, but the most august sovereign inspecting his vast estates never had the grandiloquent aplomb that flies from this mutt's face as he takes full cognizance of the passing surroundings.

In the field, the garden, venerable man and beast make a strange team. A hundred yards from the garden, the busy street chokes and splutters with the racket of machines. And the plow is really inconsistent when an unseen jet passes overhead, leaving a stream of tea-kettle steam in the form of a morning calling card. So, why a plow amid all this profusion of science? Why, indeed, a vegetable garden when the supermarket, a stone's throw distant, is a gleaming horticultural Eden?

But love of the land, especially in the South, is the one continuous unifying force. This affection is demonstrated by the hapless farmer who fights to hold his land as if it were his honor. It is seen as a consistent ritual in thousands of small flower and vegetable plots. It even fights for tangible manifestation when it can be expressed only in the rigid confinement of a few furtive pots or window boxes. People still ride in their cars to survey the fields. When a hard rain comes, followed by intense heat, some city folks still say: "Somebody's corn field will be sprouting weeds."

So you get the impression that the motion of the plow, an almost imperceptible ripple, will outlast all the dipsy-doodles of international politics. The colored man, the decrepit horse, and the plow go on eternally to nowhere, but nowhere may be the place in which the heart and the treasure are deposited. The old plowman puts his faded jacket at the end of a row when ritual commences. The dog lies and sits on the jacket, overseeing the day's work. As the sun turns up his thermostat constantly, the old man moves the jacket to shaded places. And at lunch time, man, horse, and dog are in a circle breaking together their humble fare. It is the kind of picture a rustic artist might paint so he could come back 100 years hence and things would be as they were before.

When late afternoon is besmirched with gray hair and dark wrinkles, the ancient horse heads homeward with frightening stolidity. Surely, the horse will expire, the wagon will become a heap of kindling in the street, and the fagged plowman and the dog will vanish into the evening dew. The whole procession might be called illusion did not the whanging hooves conspire with the concrete street to send fireflies spiraling toward the sunset. But along the street the children turn from Superman to the consternation and awe of a horse and wagon and plow in 1960. Aren't horses just on television, wagons loose boards in junk yards, and plows ferric acid?

Sssh—the Fish Won't Bite

The pole fisherman with his can of worms must be anachronistic today when so much emphasis is on casting. Today, the average fisherman spends as much money on fancy flies, intricate reels, boats, and camping equipment as his father spent on groceries for a year.

There seems to be some pond or lake, some natural or artificial body of water, in almost every section. Each year, more and more people go to the oceans for deep-sea fishing. Yet the worm man still seeks the docile creek or shaded pond. Long ago he fell helplessly in love with the little rivers, the jaunty streams whose names ought to be spelled in lower case letters. For him, nothing is so fascinatingly soothing as the gentle waters that carry elfin songs in their silver lips.

The progress of this water is slow. It isn't trying to be an epic, or a thumping narrative poem in the manner of the great surging river. The little trickles have a billion various moods and colors. The tiny ripples go on forever to nowhere, leaving trails for forget-me-nots in the guise of polished stones, swirling mosses, and tiny but buoyant watered shoots.

These little waters delight the eye and intoxicate the mind but their small lullabies are to the heart the honey and myrrh of unutterable peace.

The fisherman finds a tree and he makes himself as comfortable as Rip Van Winkle. His lunch is in one hip pocket and the other hip pocket usually has a book, or newspapers or magazines, or perhaps some crossword puzzles. Were it not for his droopy eyelids he would be a facsimile of Rodin's "Thinker." He may not be innately anti-social but he welcomes conversation about as much as McSorley's saloon welcomed Carrie Nation.

When some polite, well-meaning interloper asks him if he is having any luck, he smiles benignly and places his finger vertically across his mouth to indicate silence. He pretends he's getting a bite. Naturally, he has known for years that fish have ears for balance, that a fish is aware of vibrations but is not aware of sounds. Yet, for many generations man and his fellows have purchased silence with the counterfeit currency that talk will disturb the fish, keep them from biting.

When twilight is a mellow apple hanging in the sky, the pole fisherman never measures his luck by the number or size of the fish. Frequently, his luck is almost astounding when there isn't a shiner in the poke. He's had hours of uninterrupted meditation and cogitation. The little symphonies and the moving galleries of the water have banished oppression and left in its stead a humming docility that is laid in store for the morrow's perturbations. The pole fisherman is one of the last of the precious tribe for whom time has no appalling tendency to haste. These hours of sunshine are to be savored and put in trust to keep off an influx of falling inner weather.

The Belled Buzzard of Granville County

A number of year ago Irvin S. Cobb wrote and published a short story called the "Belled Buzzard." This fact is noted because the Cobb story had considerable publicity among readers of a vanished era, and may yet be found in some of the older college anthologies. Irvin Cobb was a sharp observer and no doubt his story is an admirable fusion of assorted facts, Kentucky folklore, and local anecdotes.

But in this tale before you, there is no fusion of fancy and fact. Certainly not as I have written it down. Any embellishments are the inadvertent dross that accumulates when tales are passed from the facile lips of one generation to the next.

This is a tiny piece of localized history about an infamous buzzard that used to appear, with all the dark music of a black mass, and perch atop the belltower of the courthouse in Oxford, N. C., whenever a death sentence was about to be passed by the presiding judge of the Granville County Superior Court. Away back then, criminals were executed, by hanging, in a big yard between the courthouse and jail (gaol). There was no central prison for such executions. This buzzard would come while court was in session, even before the jury reached its harrowing verdict, it has been told. Not always, of course. But there is little doubt the buzzard did appear a few times while the jury was still deliberating.

The buzzard didn't always return for the hanging. That is, he wasn't always seen but old folks would swear they heard rasping, funeral music, a discord of chains being rattled the night before the execution. That might have been due to over-active imaginations. Yet, no one ever saw the buzzard unless the infamous beast was atop the belltower.

He was a black shadow in that no one knew whence he came or went. Suddenly in the middle of the day the loathsome monster would be atop the courthouse. Yet when people started rehashing the news, no one could ever remember seeing him come or go. It was even suggested he was an optical illusion, but he was real enough. For, one day some damned fools shot off some of his evil feathers.

Now today, hardly anyone has ever seen a belled buzzard. In our society, it is almost hideously preposterous to think of anyone's having the unmitigated temerity to put his hands on a damned buzzard, much less to affix a bell. But in many Southern rural communities there is one patriarch who remembers vividly hearing about some belled buzzard. Mind you, the patriarch doesn't say he actually saw one, but he knew about the despicable existence of one.

Everyone may not be actually physically afraid of a buzzard but no one wants to fool with one, with or without a bell. Just about everyone wants a lot of daylight between himself and this insolent poltroon that strikes goose pimples from afar. A lone buzzard in a dead tree (buzzard tree) is as diabolical as a snake charming a bird. The idiot bird could fly away, if it used its wits and wings. But wherever the damnable buzzard flies, death flies also, or, even more starkly, death is waiting in a crumpled heap at the station.

The buzzard is more insolent than a craven atop a wall with a switch-blade knife under his shirt. The buzzard gives you a queasy feeling deep down in your guts. He induces a blood-twisting fear, more psychological than physical, perhaps. The filthy buzzard induces the same dread you feel at the mention of some horrible epidemic. Seeing the slimy buzzard wheeling listlessly inside and outside the carcass of a dead cow or mule gnaws your guts so powerfully you really think you can hear the reverberation. He makes you feel as if a leper is clutching at you in the darkness. You are in one of those frightful dreams when motion is lost and horror is jet-propelled.

If you are a motorist you know the terrific compulsion to run down the buzzard on the highway. But when you get close you are so careful to avoid contact you would tear the car to hell and back before you'd hit one lousy feather. No force on earth could wash away the tainted blood of a buzzard.

Did you ever notice a real dirt farmer when he sees a buzzard? He never mentions the word without appending son-of-a-bitch or bastard. The farmer sees the scavenger. The farmer spits with silent, frigid fury, and rattles with a ferocious mumble: "Sonofabitchingbuzzard. Bastardbuzzard." But despite the small sizzling vituperation, the farmer keeps right on walking, sharply away from the sonofabitchingbuzzard.

A lot of folks in the country used to say a buzzard was deaf. Admittedly he is almost impervious to stones and shouts. He may move from the dead tree but he moves with studied insolence, with a malignant insolence that his effortless motions just keep from being insufferable arrogance. Like a muted devil he seems to whisper: "O.K. sonny boy. Yell out your lungs. Throw your arm off. I got plenty of time. I am all of Poe's conquering worms come together in one set of slimy black wings."

When I was a boy all kids believed buzzards were immune to death. They were vastly more prevalent back then because few folks buried dead animals, and the highway department folks didn't clean up messes the way they do now. In every small town and rural community there were the witch-trees or buzzard trees. Even the grass and shadows that lay about these dead trees seemed contaminated. No one ever climbed a buzzard tree. Good God no. A buzzard might come back and the smallest thing that happened would be that you'd break your neck trying to get away. Superstitious folks said a buzzard's shadow would kill the grass about the dead tree.

That, of course, is poppycock, but for a petrified fact, grazing cows and chickens always gave buzzard tree shadows a wide berth. Maybe they still do and maybe they don't but they damned surely used to.

In the innocent era, when boys got their first .22 rifles or .410 gauge shotguns they potted away at the buzzards, always at a safe distance. But everyone knew you couldn't kill a buzzard. Many times I have known that I hit one. I could hear the bullet strike the harrowing bone or see a ghastly feather fly. I had a young friend named William and we shot at the scavengers together. Together we must have fired a thousand shells and cartridges at the sonofabitchingbuzzards. But we knew all the time that we wouldn't kill one. We doubted a French 75 would kill one. This was right after World War I and we asked my uncle, a soldier, if a 75 shell would kill a bastardbuzzard.

He said: "Boy, you are crazy in the head and the foot, also. If a buzzard ever flew across the Argonne Forest, ten minutes later there wouldn't be a doughboy or Hun any closer than Berlin and Paris."

To get back to the main story, the one about the belled buzzard in Oxford. There was a fellow named Wilcox tried one time for murder. He swore and be damned if he wasn't in Virginia at the time of the crime. Trouble was he couldn't produce a witness. This man Wilcox said he was possum hunting with a man named Ed Byrd on the night of the murder. But no one could ever locate this Ed Byrd.

The prosecutor argued this Ed Byrd didn't exist except in Wilcox's imagination. To condense the story, the jury got the case and went out to confer, and some people along the street started babbling about the belled buzzard being atop the belltower. Perhaps, it had been a long time since the buzzard had been in Oxford. Maybe, the buzzard came during the night. If so, he wasn't noticed until the jury went to deliberate its verdict. The jury room is just off the court room, on the second floor of the building. But the jurors could hear the talk on the streets below. And if they were men of any imagination at all, they could feel the buzzard on the belltower above them. They could feel his horrendous presence. If they couldn't see the buzzard they must have felt that the buzzard could see through the roof down upon them.

The jury convicted this man Wilcox. The judge passed the death sentence. Everyone in the court room was babbling nervously about the belled buzzard. They were huddled together, their heads down, as if from a sense of protection. The judge beat for order several times. The nervous chattering went right ahead, and some man said he would ring the bell and the buzzard would leave. The bell beat a dirge but the buzzard didn't move. He was even uglier and more insolent. A crowd came running from all over Oxford. Some thought there was a fire and others thought an alarm was being rung.

The prisoner, Wilcox, broke loose from the sheriff. He leaped from a window and he broke his neck on the cobblestones below. Wilcox had a brother, and this brother grabbed a shotgun and emptied both barrels at the belled buzzard. Some loose feathers spiraled down slowly as evil ashes from a burning haunted house.

Several fights started. Some wanted to track down the buzzard and kill it gruesomely. Others screamed imprecations. No, no. It would be against all the customs. Besides, you couldn't kill this buzzard. Don't anger him. Leave it alone and it will get tired of Oxford and drift away.

The buzzard did glide away. Many people saw its tantalizing flight and swore to the fact afterwards. But the next day it was back on the perch again. The presence on the belltower the second day was hideous, paganly so. For, no one was being tried for a capital crime, if, indeed, court was still in session.

The next day, the second day, this brother of Wilcox's, the same who had fired at the buzzard, was found dead halfway between Oxford and Shoo-fly, his home ten miles from Oxford. The horse he had been riding was gone, gone forever, they told it. It was obvious that Wilcox's brother had been thrown. His back was broken and he was fearfully scarred and cut. There were terrible abrasions, deep and wicked ones that could have come from a horse's iron foot or maybe they came from a blow from a rock. The horse may have thrown and trampled him. Or he may have been thrown and his head struck the rock. Some whispered he had been waylaid and robbed. A few muttered, behind closed doors, that the buzzard waited for Wilcox's brother, swooped down and killed the man or made him kill himself from agonizing terror.

This theory came from something said by the schoolmaster in Oxford. The schoolmaster came to the courthouse square and told the story in Coleridge's poem, "The Rime of the Ancient Mariner." The schoolmaster talked about the eerie albatross in the poem, about the shooting of the bird. He also recounted several stories reflecting albatross lore and superstition.

So, many people in Oxford decided there was a judgment on Wilcox's brother. The buzzard was tied in with the albatross, immediately and irrevocably. Wilcox's brother was killed because he shot at the belled buzzard. If the buzzard didn't do the actual job, itself, the heinous judgment killed the man.

It was a judgment and the judgment might lie on the entire community. It was a strange night, the night Wilcox's brother was killed. Somebody remembered seeing an elderberry bush burning that night, burning as brightly as a fire in a parlor grate. Several others saw blood on the moon, a great blotch of it.

Actually, the omens of ill seen are too numerous for recitation. A house burned in which no one had made a fire. Somebody killed a pig, cut its throat and the shoat didn't squeal once. A chicken with its fool neck wrung off walked three miles scattering blood in the manner of weird and appallingly ominous hieroglyphics. The crows in the forests that ringed Oxford cawed all night, as if seeking some urgent request that wasn't supplied and whose absence intensified the shattering caw-caw-cawing.

Maybe, most of these unaccountable events can be charged off to primitive superstition or to alert imaginations. More likely, they are coincidences, but each grisly tidbit came back to the damning words of the schoolmaster and his correlation between the sonofabitchingbelledbuzzard and the albatross in the Coleridge poem.

The second day, the day after the trial, the day the belled buzzard returned, if he ever left, a man came into the bar room in Oxford and said his name was Ed Byrd. He said he knew nothing about Wilcox being tried for murder. He said, why yes, it was true about him and Wilcox and the possum hunt on the night of the murder.

The other bar patrons spoke up angrily. They said this was the damndest yet. Why, this fellow Ed Byrd could have cleared Wilcox. Why in hell hadn't he showed up at the trial? What the hell, they said, Virginia wasn't on the other side of the world but jam against Granville County in North Carolina. This bastard could have saved an innocent life.

You understand how tempers were, how much consternation and chagrin followed the deaths of Wilcox and his brother and all the fantastic events of the night, the night following the trial. Somebody came in from the street and heard Ed Byrd's story. The bar patrons had merely listened up to now, but this man from the street ran out and brought back a crowd, as many as 25 or 30, possibly. They said the only way of evening the score, of putting baleful matters right, was to hang this Ed Byrd. All around the square the cry went up: Hang him. Hang him, high as Haaman.

Somebody got a rope in the hardware store and the mob set out for the big alley behind the courthouse. The official scaffold wasn't up, none had been used recently, and they were going to hang this Ed Byrd to a tree. They put the rope about his neck and when they gave him the opportunity for some last words he tried to tell them how wrong they were. He hadn't done anything. He didn't even know Wilcox had been accused of anything.

The mob wouldn't have it, not a lame word of it all. The only feasible way to remove the terrible judgment was to eliminate the author of all the misery. This fellow Byrd in some inexplicable manner, some nebulous fashion, was the root of all the madness.

Just as they were getting ready to put him on a horse, the alley was swept with the maddening sounds of a slowly tolled bell.

They had forgotten about the buzzard. This fellow Ed Byrd had diverted the wrath, absorbed some of the tingling fear. They say, they said, it is told that the bell on the buzzard dingled as if a shroud were being stitched with steel.

The belled buzzard swooped down over the mob. From the way it has been told to me, the buzzard buzzed, like a fighter plane, and swept to the right, wheeled back to the left and came back with increased force. The mob ran into one another. Some hid in corners and behind shrubs. Some ran headlong for the street. There was no direction in this panic. The only motivation was escape. The belled buzzard flew just above the heads of the crowd. He flew up and down the alley, turning, wheeling, and coming back again and again.

They say this Ed Byrd spoke some low words to the belled buzzard, that the buzzard sat on a tree limb above this Ed Byrd's head, listening closely. (Since the mob had dispersed, pell-mell, this must have been seen from a distance, but it was sworn and reaffirmed that the buzzard perched on Ed Byrd's shoulder for a second.) This Ed Byrd spoke some final words and the belled buzzard flew off into a white cloud and disappeared.

This time the people saw him when he left, saw him when he entered the white cloud. And that belled buzzard hasn't been seen in Granville County since that awful day.

This Ed Byrd stayed in Oxford a few years after the belled buzzard left. He amassed a small fortune gambling. No one wanted to play cards with this Ed Byrd but everyone was afraid not to play, afraid to win, afraid the infamous buzzard might return. Behind his back and behind their hands and doors, folks referred to Ed Byrd as Lazarus. Some whispered he was a strange kind of leper. He was the "belled buzzard man." They say the grass didn't grow where he spat. He had no friends but no material enemies, either. No one walked beside him on the street but everyone was overly courteous, foppishly so, when they passed this Ed Byrd.

Then one day he vanished. No one saw him leave. He was gone. That was all, just gone. There have been ten thousand tales about where he went and what he did. He was a road agent out west, a millionaire up north, a card sharp on ocean liners, and he was even in some President's cabinet under an assumed name.

All of this was a long time ago, but even to this hour when the sky is black crepe and the wind moans the way chains rattle, some old man in Granville County will look furtively all around and whisper throatily: "It's a season of this Ed Byrd weather. If you hear a tiny bell, run for your life. It's him, this Ed Byrd and that sonofabitchingbelledbuzzard, and ain't no atom bomb in creation can do more'n knock a feather or hair outa either one of them."

'Po' Man and His Dog

Back in the days when political leaders were identified with specific songs, Speaker of the House Champ Clark's adherents paraded to the sassy, sashaying strains of:

"Now, I don't care if he is a hound
You better not kick my dog around."

At the Democratic Convention at Baltimore in 1912, it took an unprecedented number of ballots before Champ Clark and his rollicking hound dog music were vanquished by the austere and somber refrain of Woodrow Wilson.

Certainly, the sprightly music didn't make Champ Clark the formidable political leader he was. Yet, when people thought of Champ Clark they thought of hound dogs and hound dog music. This pleasantly ingratiating combination has never hurt any aspirant. Basically speaking, elegant and blooded dogs are for fanciers. Ordinary folks love ordinary dogs. Some of the sorriest looking dogs in town have received the most affection. It is almost as if the shabby dog knows he's a poor spectacle, that awareness of this crystallizes into tender understanding. It is almost as if the dog said: "I may not be much to look at but by ardor and devotion I will make you forget about my sad face and shaggy coat."

The mutual esteem of dog and master is celebrated in thousands of poems and songs. Usually, though, these legends deal with dogs of superior talents, with dogs that perform memorable feats. There is yet this other dog, unsung and generally unwanted, whose charm lies in possession. This is the untutored pot-likker the poor man raised, or found, saved from the pound, or nursed back to health after community neglect. His apparent talent lies only in his availability. He's good for eating cornbread and drinking pot-likker.

This circumscribed fare reflects his owner's station in life. Most of the time neither man nor animal will ever get a vote for anything but being handy. And yet only an atom bomb can separate the two. The man will actually give the dog his own bread, when the bedraggled master is hungry, himself. The man nurses the dog with touching fidelity. When the man stumps his own toe, the dog goes into prodigious mourning.

Human society being what it is, the 'po' man, the undernourished, uninspired piece of human flotsam is subjected to regular abuse. This abuse is normally based on nothing more than the penchant of mankind to want to have something to feel superior to, to cherish meanly the hapless drudge who can be made the butt of mild derision and distorted humor. The poor man seems more impervious to this scorn than the dog. When the master goes down town to spend his rapidly melting coppers, men along the street ask if he earned the money singing a solo in church, or writing a deed, or did a rich uncle die in Texas? If this man, who subsists on odd jobs, who does for short pay what others are too proud to do for themselves, sits down in a store other men want to know why he's resting? Hasn't he been resting for 50 years, they jestingly ask? And this wretched piece of dog meat. Why doesn't he feed this thing to the crows for Sunday dinner? Or sarcasm takes a right oblique, and the other men want to know if this remarkable creature didn't win a blue ribbon at the dog show in Madison Square Garden?

The dog laughs and wags his tail. You just know this mutt realizes he is being buffeted with ridicule but he laughs the way certain menials laugh when joked by their more affluent and imposing elders. But the dog reacts differently when the 'po' man gets the point of the satire between the eyes. He growls and he snaps and he has to be led to a safe place quickly.

Maybe, an expert would point out that dogs are not so perceptive as this piece contends. Yet it is undeniably and unalterably true that the dog can tell when the critic is talking about it and when he is talking about the master. A street loafer says: "Why I could whittle a better dog out of a piece of bark." The dog wags his tail and grins foolishly. When the sentence is: "I could whittle a better man out of a piece of bark than sorry Rufus Brown," the dog gets up his dander and barks it around the premises.

The relationship between the po' man and his dog is a happy and a necessary one—for most men and most dogs. But just as among people we find lovers of the universal rather than of the specific, there are, in dogdom, whimsical practitioners of the hobo art.

In every small town there's still a dog that belongs to no one, specifically, and to everyone, generally. Where he came from no one knows. If he has any permanent lodging quarters, no one knows where to address his mail from day to day. The whole town is his boarding house. He may eat hors d'oeuvres in an alley, the main course at the banker's kitchen door, and he may take his dessert when the fire truck driver has his.

He helps the street cleaners for a while, watches a baseball game on a vacant lot, and then saunters to the "time" store to catch up on the political news. He has no credit cards, credentials, or collar but if Stonewall Jackson were the local dog warden he wouldn't have the guts to put this mutt in the pound. Fishermen take him to the ponds and children invite him to their parties. He goes to court and to the picture show. At one time or other he has ridden on the front seat of every delivery truck in town. When he's tired he naps in the lobby of the post office or on the cool boards in the hall right outside a lawyer's office.

He's been to school so many times he'd be able to do algebra, if education were really contagious. He's ridden round at night with lonely doctors so often you half expect him to lecture at the medical society. He's a mutt, all right, but the mayor gives him elbow room on the sidewalk. When the sun punches the time clock and the velvet evening takes charge, you almost expect the night policeman to ask this mongrel for instructions. If he ever got a better job in a bigger town, you'd have to drape the courthouse square with black crepe.

Toys for the Hogs

It's a stony fact, if a bewildering one, that certain county agents and assorted experts are strongly advising hog raisers to put toys in the pens. It seems that the railing pen and the hog wallow are incompatible with the expanding facets of the modern pig's personality, and hogs no longer forage for loose condiments. The current domicile is the "feeding parlor."

The feeding parlor makes the old pen shabby as a dingy tenement, but the hogs can't stray beyond the formal limits of their new premises. Restriction, though, induces recalcitrance. They become fractious and bite off each other's tails.

After certain diligent county agents had investigated this appalling situation, they went up on the mountain and came down with the panacea: Give the hogs toys to play with and the restive eruptions will be allayed.

The trouble now is the toys will be bound to induce squeals and peals incident to new social consciousness. The imminent pork chops with the toy space gun will feel too high and mighty to have any truck with his neighbor that has only a rubber ball. The gal hog with the miniature kitchen set will shun her old playmate who has only some jack-rocks. The fattening hog will be given toy golf sticks, probably. His skinny chum that has only dumb-bells will hate his insides. The result of these toys is bound to be a gang war.

Soon, hog toy departments will probably be in all our venerable "time" stores. To one side of the guano, between that and the plow points, will be the toy shop. When Bertha outgrows her kiddie car, the farmer will be hard put to decide between a toy motorcycle or a little do-it-yourself beauty kit.

There will, of course, be one gigantic socio-economic problem: The hogs that live on Erskine Caldwell's farms will get nothing for Christmas, or for Easter, for that matter. However, some self-effacing civic club will rally round the hog pen, and right in the middle of Tobacco Road there will be a scrumptious hog-tree laden with bright baubles. This will probably be the first time in the history of pork that a piece of sausage carried its own sack.

Dragons versus Science

When summer casts her lambent-conjured spell there's still time after supper for a delightful hour of play. The night gets fatter and lazier every day. Sometimes you almost have to chunk rocks to get him on the job. The lights and half-lights of the gloaming are tender and juicy and they taper down to fragile and nostalgic edges at utter twilight.

The child races from the supper table, his mouth resembling a log jam in a river. He bounds to the front door on two sizzling wheels and gasps: "May I be scuzed, pleze." There is not a question mark. Before the mother has time to swallow and speak, the boy is in the yard. The yard is a fairyland filled with magic games. All the neighborhood tots gather at an inaudible signal, and the late afternoon breeze has to push and shove just to gain standing room in the yard. The buoyancy of playing, the ingenuity of innovation, sweep the face of creation, but beyond the laughter, there are dragons behind the hedgerows and trees. Across the street and around the corner there are lions and tigers, and those man-made monsters you see on the advertisements in front of the movie houses.

"Little Orphant Annie" may not be read today but kids still chant: "And the gobbleuns'll git you if you don't watch out." Really, though, these scientific brats put little stock in "gobbleuns," but if any of James Whitcomb Riley's spooks were out, the riot of nervous laughter would wash them away, send them scurrying. A fig for supernatural specters and several dozen prunes for fears. A toy space gun can kill the most ferocious dragon, and anyone knows a headless horseman couldn't pass his driver's license test.

True, Frankenstein's monster has had more lives than a crate of cats. His resurrections are whole-blood to the late, late TV shows. But this monster is such an awkward big jerk, you can trip him with a skipping rope and scare him to death with a handful of lightning bugs. This fiend was completely terrified by fire in Mrs. Shelley's day, and, now, as old as he is, one flashlight would send him, hippity-hop, clean over the Bavarian Alps.

And yet merriment is the one unbeatable charm to fend off all alarms. Laughter is a tonic that turns deterrent. Kids use laughter against spooks the same way the old-timers shot off cannons to disperse the miasma that was thought to induce fever.

No matter how sophisticated today's brat is, no matter how far his scientific investigation proceeds, when he comes back into the house to take his bath, he has a strange sense of having gone to the South Seas with Herman Melville, of having lived among cannibals, but outwitted these devils, and of returning home safely charged with the luster of perilous adventure.

Chicken Wars and Chicken Catchers

Today, even in small towns, chickens roost in ice boxes in supermarkets or in a deep-freeze in the home. Only day before yesterday, most folks in small towns kept a few chickens, some fryers and some laying hens, too. A few proud and energetic people made hen nests of straw and boards. However, most of the chickens roosted in a tree in the chicken lot, when they had the energy to flap up to the limbs.

According to the vegetable gardeners, the neighbors' chickens spent so much time and labor foraging they were too tired to get back home at night, much less to flounder-fly to a tree perch. For a fact, fowls did stray and they got fat in the neighboring gardens. Full scale chicken wars ensued. Bloodshed was at a minimum but the intensity of the running contention between the vegetable man and the chicken man approached that of the range wars between cattle and sheep men.

Some fervent gardeners, those who made a high art of production and attractiveness, hated chickens so venomously they wouldn't permit it served at the table, not even if the governor came visiting. A few militant defenders of the corn and butterbeans shot chickens and they shot to kill. In most localities, shooting to kill wasn't resorted to until repeated verbal and written warnings had been dispatched to the poultry owner. Occasionally, some irate man would jump on the person of the owner, himself.

A few gardeners let this rancor grow until it absorbed all waking minutes and induced cackling nightmares. After due warning, they shot on sight. They would pick up the lifeless carcass with paper or pliers and fling it on the porch of the owner. This was done in much the same spirit that old man Ike Clanton is said to have gunned down one of the Earp lads and then deposited the body on the porch of Marshal Wyatt Earp's office.

Naturally, violent action was fairly rare. Occasionally, some man peppered the marauders with a load made of fatback and hard beans. This did no more than remove a couple of tail feathers and raise a blister. To be truthful, the fatback and beans load was used more freely than the lethal charge. No one bothered about this home-made piece of ordnance because it was standard equipment for boys who stole apples and for nice swains who tried, nonetheless, to keep trysts with nice girls, after bedtime.

The overwhelming majority of aggrieved chicken victims tried to devise snide tricks that would embarrass the owner of the flock. The gardener really tried to keep the pesky birds out, and he sat up trying to imagine impenetrable fences. Frequently, he spent more money on wire, boards, and bricks than a small truck farm cost. Yet, this was always a shattering waste of labor and jack. For, even if the chicken is as stupid as alleged, she has no trouble going underneath, over, around, or through any kind of obstruction that does not contain land mines.

So, to harass the owner, the vegetable man baited fishing hooks with worms or grains of corn. The fool chicken would blunder and bounce around the neighborhood dragging a light bamboo pole in her idiotic mouth. However, this was ineffective and, actually, destructive. Before the string was cut from the pole the average chicken could wreck a trillion growing plants.

Still, there was always one gardener whose humor was excessively sardonic. On the fishing hook line he tied a printed sign that read: "I am a bad chicken. I am a vegetable thief. I belong to Mr. Horace Entwhistle, 110 Magnolia Street."

Ever so often, someone would bait a chicken coop. After he

had caught three or four he would drive to a neighboring town and send the crate C.O.D. to the owner. The trip back and forth was more expensive but the perpetrator of the hoax knew that everyone in town would ask the recipient-owner if he got any nice out-of-town gifts, lately.

All of this wasn't so far back, not as the crow of time flies. In light of social change, though, it was long ago. There is a charcoal grill where the idiot chickens roosted and a new street has been cut across the vegetable garden. Insularity is old-hat, even in small places. Some things don't die, however, despite the turn from superficial provinciality to nationalism. Children who hadn't even been thought of, even in wishful dreaming, know all about the ancient chicken wars. Even in 1960 as the erstwhile gardener walks the streets some maniac, well-hidden, will cackle and beat his arms to simulate fluttering wings. And the older citizens still refer to him as "Mr. Chicken Hotchkiss," at a safe distance and in very small voices, naturally.

When people stopped keeping chickens, a lucrative juvenile profession expired. In every neighborhood there were professional chicken-catchers. Before the magic freezing devices, you cooked your own fryers but first you had to catch them. Chickens were always unpredictable but on big in little pot days, they were elusive as the Scarlet Pimpernel. Many housewives were afraid to touch a live chicken. Many were appalled at decapitation. Many recent brides, those who could still smell the salt and the taffy at Atlantic City, avoided any encounter that might taint their living hands. Others lacked the clothing or dexterity to climb trees, crawl under houses, or to penetrate brambles, briars, and honeysuckle.

Boys gradually formed semi-formal unions. Clients were the hapless and frail, spinsters, and women with small children. Ordinarily, the catcher received a nickel for a ground chase and a dime for an aerial performance. The catchers knew precisely when a given housewife needed fresh meat. The eating habits of neighbors were known as intimately back then as their credit ratings and bank balances are now known. If company was coming, making chicken mandatory at an irregular night, the union knew this, too. If the fool hen or fryer stood docilely at the back door, the boys didn't throw fits nearly so often as rocks.

When times were really parlous, or if a circus or show came to town, the union dragged worms to lure the chickens in the neighbor's garden. This was a form of mass kidnapping. For these situations a flat contract of from 25 to 50 cents for the lot was enforced. It was a two-pronged collusion. The baiting of the whole caboodle was done when the gardener was up town working. His wife was telephoning him frantically just as one of the chicken-catching union dropped along. Usually, the same fee was extracted from the gardener that the housewife paid.

There were about five kids in the average union, three to scout business and two to be on hand to apprehend vagrant fowls. Just as the Chicago gangsters did, these boys had specific town boundaries. The Magnolia Street union never did any luring or procuring in the Whitehaven Section. Once or twice, some families might go vegetarian, temporarily, or others might have to subscribe to some religious or dietary regimen that precluded meat at given times. Then, there was slight invasion of another union's territory. This perfidy was settled by legal arbitration or by fists and skulls, rather more by the latter.

Everyone in town knew the professional catcher by sight, if not by smell. Some wore feathers in their caps as trademarks and some wore feathers in their hair, inadvertently. If the school teacher told one of these boys that his hands were dirty he would reply: "Yes, ma'am, I know. I'm sorry, but you see I had to catch some black chickens early this morning."

Ants Are Idlers

Specious and spurious American mythology has long insisted that ants are the crawling epitome of industry. Ants are supposed to be as dedicated to unvarnished labor as the old-time movie comedians were to custard pies.

The truth is that ants are the playboys of the insect world. Ants have spent as many effortless hours in the purling sunshine as the lilies of the fields. In the insect world the ant is thought of as we thought of the small-town loafer whose sole activity was delivering the clothes his wife washed, when, of course, he was up to the task. Ants are just like these venerable loafers. They are simple obstructionists and their tenuous value lies solely in the ability to compound a frightful nuisance.

The squirrel, with a wise eye cocked against an influx of falling weather, lays up vast stores against the morrow. The robin, emulating the parsimony of Silas Marner, hoards old pieces of string and bits of shoe boxes. Whereas, the ant keeps waiting for social security checks he will never get because of uninterrupted unemployment.

The ant divides his time between the public park and the lakeside. He is straight from the pattern of the old-time bum who spent all his waking hours trying to learn which saloons were having free lunches. He is exactly like the lazy, indolent relative who makes all his visits coincide with mealtime. Were it not for his small stature, he would have been sent to the roads for vagrancy by the park policemen or the Shore Patrol.

In summer, when the earth is a buzzing, humming wheel singing paeans to high endeavor, the ant sports in the soft sand until a hand-out comes along in the form of a picnic. Unlike the old-fashioned back door hobo, he will not eat his snack and depart. He hates his benefactor and he hangs around all day to

41

harass and pester. He is a first cousin of the village "radical" who hates everyone who has as much as four dollars because he is too good-for-nothing to work, himself. The ant goes about the park and the lakeside haranguing the summer balm with self-pitying petitions of exploitation. The picnickers are the lazy rich who are feasting on blood of the oppressed. But the ant, according to his baleful imprecation, was snatched from his mother's knee at a tender age and sent straight to the mill.

While the crow went off to study elocution, the beaver engineering, and the snake legerdemain, the hapless ant mortgaged his tender soul to the company store. So what's the use now? The system is too vicious, but if you can create the false impression you are the soul of diligence you can get an international reputation and very few folks will muster the gall to say, aloud, you just aren't worth a damn, you ant, you.

The Twilight Weepers and the Little Creatures

The willow tree, weeping by the water's edge, is a supplicant bent in penitence. This impression is particularly telling when the twilight casts her spell. The twilight is an old woman tossing flakes of gray from her apron pockets. She comes to herd up all of earth's creatures together to take them to a quiet and sustaining lodging and rest.

At eventide, the wind is a collie dog rounding up the last of the strays. The willows by the water's edge chant a spirited lamentation. The wind in the willows isn't so much a dirge as a running summary of poignant meditation. When the wind shakes willow leaves onto the water, there is the notion of the talismen in the sea. But these talismen are not thrown with deliberate force to invoke good luck, to placate the gods of fortune and the demi-gods of weather. The gesture is reluctant. The willow leaf on the water is a reluctant wish that isn't expected to be answered, certainly not to be answered fully.

It is easy to get the impression of self-abnegation. The willow really weeps. It doesn't rend its breast but tears are tied in with the sloping boughs that bend low and shed wet leaves so profusely. The water in the pond or pool enhances the illusion of real tears, and there is almost the positive fact of the exchanging of formal raiment for something akin to sack cloth and ashes.

As the mists of twilight fall faster, the willows huddle closer together as if the knowledge of nearness is a charm to fend off the suggestion of unknown evil that hides within the night.

For generations these weeping willows have conducted a day school for birds. Classes extend from kindergarten to high school. Here, in the school by the water's edge, are taught the sombre correlations between leaves, shadows, and birds. To call this instruction in "artful dodging" is incomplete, as well as trite. "Blending" is a better word. Or, "camouflaging" is better yet.

Willows have the knack of becoming immaterial as shadows. Late of an afternoon, or early of a morning, viewed from a slight distance, any line of weeping willows could pass muster easily as a row of shadows. Whenever a predatory force appears, this force is likely to think the willows are reflections of something else. So, they keep a school to indoctrinate birds, to impart the skills, agilities, and subtleties necessary to enable a bird to become a shadow.

But fear should be completely disassociated from this tranquillity, from this pastoral. Those who come to bathe and those who come to watch, to absorb, to read unwritten poetry, to sing songs without words surely have no predatory designs. But all little creatures must be taught to fear any footfall that comes beyond the immediate fraternity. That's probably the explanation.

The willows and the birds on the edge and the shadows and the leaves in the water form a picture straight from the Old Testament. Old-timers used to sing a sprightly tune that may still give the picture:

"Pharoah's daughter on the bank,
Little Moses in the pool."

This spectacle could be maudlin, if it were viewed alone. But there is a wonderful anodyne for too much contriteness, as depicted at the water's edge: The plowboy homeward from the fields and the workman from the job break the morbid trance. The tender joy of reassurance is a whisper, a kiss, a love song, when all the world turns homeward in the gloaming. The final tatters of bleary-eyed light say clearly to the willows and the birds, as to all who will listen:

"O Children by the water's edge,
Lift up your harps and sing."

Beyond the clearing of the water, the hare in the forest lacks the formal instruction taught by the twilight weepers. Maybe, the self-reliance that is bred of self-education is required to cope with adversaries so formidable as man's pride and lust. The hound will have him from his hole if for nothing more tangible than his master's cursory approbation. Hunted and haunted from birth, the only song he has time to learn is: "Run, rabbit, run." From the second he departs his mother's nest, terror is his companion, his evil pillar of fire by night and his menacing shield by day.

The hare wouldn't attend any school, even if invited. Every

light is an inferno and every shadow is a trap. Trust has no place in the rustic lexicon. He was born to and for man's sport. He is an elusive idiosyncrasy in man's wayward musings and meditations. His death is not even a good punch line in a stale joke, refashioned for a season's ribald satisfaction. So, run, rabbit, run, as fast and as far as you can. The weeping willows have no surcease for lust, nor any shield for shot and shell, nor any balm for death.

The big possum, though, walks just before day. He has learned every ruse the coon knows and the coon knows every bit of trickery and quacksavery the possum has accumulated. The possum is a fat man who fights when cornered but one who never spent enough time doing push-ups or handling dumb-bells. His neighbor, the coon, will fight as quick and as dangerously as Bedford Forrest. Many a hound now on the dole knows the gnashing, splashing prowess of his fury. He gets his tail cut off and his guts exposed to the moonlight, now and again, but he's as hard to swallow as a running roll of barbed wire. And the biggest coons and the fattest possums learned centuries ago the smallest tree is the hardest for the pursuer to climb. Contrawise, the littlest coons and possums will climb trees so big and tall the average hound gets acute vertigo just from trying to see the upmost limbs.

No one wants to hurt a nuthatch. If such a person existed, he couldn't hurt the nuthatch because he couldn't hold his gun straight for the paroxysms of laughter.

Some folks say the nuthatch is really demented. Hence, the use of the term as a place of incarceration for the abundantly neurotic. But it's difficult for the layman to tell where ebullience leaves off and aberration begins. The nuthatch is a spiritual wastrel who lays up no stores for the morrow's terse interrogations. He scampers around in a devastating circle as rapidly and jerkily as a show horse in the ring that doesn't give a damn about the judges but is cavorting so merrily for his very own edification. The nuthatch is the top-sergeant in a game of "Follow the leader" that never ends. You can almost hear him saying: "Here I come, ready or not."

Perpetually hell-bent-for-leather, he might use the services of a tutor but not a protector. Self-preservation is in each convolution, each tempestuous wing-ding. The hunted hare knows the nuthatch is off his beam. The hunted hare never utters a "by your leave" when he scampers to his hole at the breaking of a twig. Be the sound only a falling stick or a man with the gun, the nuthatch reacts only in the spontaneous pleasure of unexpected company. The deep woods hold a million rings and he is the master of each. Citizens of the forest think of him with the passive charity town folks bestow on the man who has talked so long and so glibly no one has heard a word he's said in forty years.

Some folks say the nuthatch's colossal recklessness is the result of his having "gotten religion" at the camp meetings conducted by Bishop Sparrow. As anyone who has ever been in the woods knows, the sparrow is the unchallenged revivalist of the forest. The sparrow translates winter's waste into sin, and he preaches against the tag ends of groping despondency as if the sheer weight of impassioned oratory will grind the inclement residue into powder.

The sparrow wants to make the world jump from the middle of March to the first day of July in one step, without changing shoes. Bishop Sparrow inveighs against gloom with the violent volubility Billy Sunday heaped on the publicans. He'd as soon browbeat a black-gum tree as a hill of sportive ants. He's a small wind shaking the vegetation, ruffling feathers and fur and arresting the constitutionals of the benign snakes.

No matter what fetish assails the woodlands, no matter what diversion sets in, the Bishop can always count on the nuthatch. The nuthatch has taken a million pledges, and he has reaffirmed his faith in sunny weather every time the Bishop has conducted a revival meeting. That's why some folks think of the nuthatch as a feathered holy roller, a wild-eyed camp-meeting convert.

Despite all his chatter, his verbal frothing, he's the essence of Huck Finn, taking his leisure where and when he wants it, giving cities a wide berth, frolicking in the sunbeams, and putting no stock in dead things.

Every community has vital need of a charming screwball, be it the ritziest, sleekest new suburb or the wildwood city whose streets are paved with pine cones and pine straw. The nuthatch is to the wilderness what the disarming gadfly is to the town. When the press of circumstance and event are almost offensive, along comes the odd-ball or nuthatch. Then it is that citizens of concrete and pine cone gather smilingly and say to one another: "Let's hurry and see what the hell that damn fool is going to say next."

It is in spring and summer that man feels real nearness to these little creatures. For, winter is the time of braving out the storm, of dragging all the warmth inside the body and inside the house. The inundation of the time of the sterile wasteland nullifies the divine desire to stay attuned to the little things beyond the window.

In the mellow time of the twilight weepers, when awareness of the world beyond the window is a persistent song rapping at the brain, the individual returns automatically to the headtaws he thinks he has forgotten. There is the long, lazy, soulful interval after supper when you sit on the porch to wait for the first star.

There is a white star above and a cricket below. The cricket, that you've forgotten ever existed, fiddles furiously as if trying to turn at least part of your attention from the star. The cricket fiddles as if strident rhythm is a tingling innovation just introduced for this particular season. The man taking his ease slaps his thigh as if a good joke has been played on him. In the gathering clusters of the night he smiles because he's found something he's always known, something that's been here a million years, but something he always forgets when he is dodging winter's clasp so assiduously.

With Mars so near, a star and a cricket may appear to be exceedingly small change. But men still bet more than money on stars and crickets. They know they can count on summer stars and crickets as they counted on their childhood gods. Since some kind of faith in something is still essential, you can do a lot worse than to bet your heart's hoarded gold on the dance of the white star, on the mad-merriment of the cricket's solo.

Birds without Wings

According to news from the veterinary institute of the University of Tokyo, the chicken of tomorrow will be wingless. This news is being hailed joyously in many places, but a chicken without wings must be akin to a bathing beauty without legs.

It has been argued for a good while that a chicken really can't soar. So, why does it need wings? It is true that a chicken, armed with the best wings, will never be an eagle. For that matter, a goat doesn't habituate the barber shop; so, why the beard?

And if chickens could fly as fast and as far and as furiously as hawks, the eggs would be well scrambled before they are ever laid. If chickens' wings enabled them to cut dexterous capers in the wild-blue-yonder, then housewives would have to spend considerably more time on the rifle range and considerably less at the beauty parlor. A chicken's wings are supposed to get it to the roost and back down again, probably for the self-same reason that Lincoln said a man's legs should be long enough to reach the ground.

The experts who plan to perfect a chicken without wings toss a utilitarian gimmick in the stew. They say that there is a little too much meat on the wings to justify throwing away and not quite enough meat on the wings to compensate for all the trouble involved in preparation. This is patently silly. A chicken must have wings when families of more than two children eat them, unless, of course, the mother is a rank vegetarian. The proper emblem for Mother's Day ought to be crossed chicken wings.

And despite the preponderance of luxurious restaurants and wayside inns, a few old-fashioned boarding houses will endure, if only to supply crude jokes. A wingless chicken in a boarding house would be as incongruous as a finger bowl in a lion's cage, worse than a snuff salesman who has an incurable case of hay fever. Actually, most of the chickens in the old-timey boarding houses had eight sets of wings, on both sides. (This was before the jet or frozen foods era.)

A billion naughty tales were told about these chicken wings, about how they would draw up three inches on the journey from the frying pan to the table. One of the best is about the consecrated proprietress who said to a boarder, with benign deference: "And how did you find your piece of chicken?"

"Hell, it won't no trouble atall. I just moved that little bitty boiled potato, and there it was, ma'am, there it was."

Poignant Saga of the Turkey

Somehow, turkey isn't so succulent as it was back yonder when it was served but a few times a year. Roast turkey in the summertime would have been as miraculous a few years ago as a Sherman Tank would have been at Gettysburg. The deep-freeze and the glistening supermarket may be adjuncts of the Big Rock Candy Mountain but children don't get nearly as excited about frozen turkeys as they did about the live ones. It takes a lot of yearning, waiting, and expectation really to step up the digestive juices to martial tempo.

In fairly recent times many families bought a turkey for Thanksgiving but they never ate this specific bird. No, he died from inertia, old age, or from the concerted servile flattery of the whole family. Another turkey was bought for the supper. The first bird was bought ostensibly to be eaten. He was put in a pen in the back yard to be fattened. Uglier than the face of original sin, the turkey bobbled around as grotesquely as a terrified fat lady on roller skates.

The children fed this monstrosity the table scraps. They talked at first of what a scrumptious meal it would make. There were arguments, nay, more, serious altercations about which child would get which piece of dark or white meat. But day by day the unbelievable homeliness of the clumsy lout fastened to the children as so many charm bracelets. The turkey ingratiated himself into protective custody. A turkey never inspired downright affection, perhaps, but the children were pervaded with the tenderest sort of compassion.

As Christmas or Thanksgiving approached, each child began to feel cannibalistic. To stay the execution of the gnomesque friend, the kids often hit upon the expedient of running the turkey until it was thin as an incredibly tall crow. Frequently, the parent knew nothing about the virtual dissolution of the imminent feast until he started to sharpen his ax.

The parent inspected the disheveled sack of bones closely, but while he was standing and pondering the suitable punishment for the children, some of the garbled charm of the wretched turkey rubbed off on him. Henceforth, the rigorous road work was suspended and the table scraps increased. Father and children agreed it was better to fatten again and to postpone the feast until next year. Naturally, everyone knew everyone else was lying through his gums. No one expected to see this barnyard brute decapitated, not next Thanksgiving or ever.

Sometimes this palpable drama, this tenuous guise, was effected because of parlous times. Some mental hocus-pocus had to shroud the rescue of the bird from the oven. This was done so that neither the parents nor the children would get wasteful ways. And again, it was done so the neighbors wouldn't say this family was curious or queer. They told the neighbors delightful little lies. One boy said they didn't eat the turkey because it had to be wormed. A little girl said the turkey's liver was out of whack. After two weeks the floundering old gobble-fowl had more ailments ascribed to him than ever listed in the veterinarians' books.

The turkey as family pet was for feeding and gazing since it was too unwieldy to tote around. Infrequently, a small child would tie a cord around the turkey's neck and lead him around, or, to be more precise, be led around. But the turkey's charm was not infectious. It was inundated in the backyard at home. The walking turkey is uglier than home-made sin foaled in last year's bird nest. To the uninitiated, its wails are as pointless as the screams of two locomotives about to collide. Perhaps, the pilgrims shot these creatures not so much for nourishment but as an object lesson in the culminative possibilities of wicked living.

The appeal lies in the pathetic barnyard picture and in the poignant saga of the tribe. There is a story in Indian mythology that blends so accurately it really ought to be accepted as factual. At the start of a certain winter the fire that kept the whole world warm went out except for a tiny spark that spluttered in a hollow tree. A turkey fanned this speck of life. The turkey's wings flailed mightily and the sparks ignited and spread. As the fire got hotter the flames crisped the feathers off the turkey's head and left a long line of blisters. That is why the old bird is blistered and bald-headed today. (The heroic turkey of the legend might have preferred raw winter, without the comfort of any fire, if he had envisioned all the scalding plucking water that would be heated by this blaze for his progeny.)

Even today, memories of turkeys or graphic pictures of the bald head and the blisters, make you so compassionate you have to think twice about asking for a third helping of white meat. Maybe.

The Goat Cart

All the goats must be butting heads in the rocky pastures of limbo. Maybe, all the local goats everyone used to know are taking turns against Goliath, Dan'l Webster's mighty billy, the one he sicked on Mr. Scratch.

Not so many years ago, a few folks in every little town milked goats. Some of these people were simple nonconformists who pretended to hate cows' milk because almost everyone else drank the stuff. A few goats' milk addicts were unlicensed medical experts. They said the milk from a goat had special medical properties. It was used, they said, regularly in Switzerland or Indiana, or some such exotic place, for the treatment of tuberculosis. A few other goat-devotees were positive the milk would not only eliminate typhoid and pellagra, but would preclude any possibility of their occurring.

There were other local scientists who declared that the person of the goat, itself, was sure-fire prevention against any serious malady. Whatever it was that came along, singly or as an epidemic, would attack the goat first. The goat had the inherent stamina to absorb anything from poison sumac to mustard gas. If, when the lethal epidemic came, the goat's horn's didn't shrivel perceptibly, the household was home-free, including the nanny.

But, of course, the goat's real popularity was as a pet and a draught animal. Often, his popularity was greater than the pony's. The upkeep was negligible. The goat solved all garbage disposal problems and made the lawn mower superfluous. He succumbed to no seasonal or dietary distresses. If he acted as if he were catching a touch of the summer complaint, you could remedy everything with a tomato can. Actually, the goat was safer than a pony, never temperamental, neurotic, or psychotic. The goat never emulated the prima donna. He was merely antisocial, supremely taciturn, and perverse as a yard full of devils.

Too, the goat spared a lot of parental care and vexation. Many parents wouldn't permit children to take a pony cart out alone. A bee might sting the pony and cause a frightful wreck, but the bee that stung a billy-goat was guilty of malicious self-destruction. A pony would shy at a shadow but the goat would lie down on a bed of dynamite and snore.

The idle rich children drove their goats to carts. (The idle rich children were those who didn't have summer jobs that carried regular stipends. Idle richers mowed lawns or sold vegetables but were not stigmatized by payroll entries, and they usually brought fifteen cent presents to birthday parties.) The cart or trap was a box-like vehicle with two wheels and one side door. The basket part was wicker and it was high enough to keep young legs from dangling over. This two-wheeler joggled just fast enough to make the passengers delightfully and deliciously skittish.

Many ten and twelve year old blades called for their lady loves in the trap. The boy and girl went for a spin. They were as lordly, in a democratic manner, as the local banker and his wife, as they smiled and nodded to the less fortunate strewn along the blistering streets and yards. But, most goats were unswervingly antagonistic to courtship. Not long after the pink-eared swain and his princess were ensconced, the goat went on a sit-down strike, right in the middle of the street, at the place that never had any shade. All sorts of bribes and threats were used. But you couldn't threaten a goat any more successfully than you could Ty Cobb. The best bait was a fresh sardine can. The can enticed the goat and the smell of sardines made him a little sick. Either way, he wanted to get home, to feast or to throw up and rest in the squalor of the chicken lot.

Other youthful masters, more utilitarian ones, hitched to little red wagons to fetch groceries and the washing and to carry passengers. On steaming mornings when parents weren't looking, the goat driver charged pennies for hauling hot little friends around the block. But some little ninny always squealed when his pennies or his credit expired. You not only had to give the whole eleven cents you had made to the Salvation Army.

You got a whipping and the goat stayed unhitched for three days.

When there was a big parade in town, on the local historic days, all the traps and wagons were decked with bunting and put in the surging hullabaloo. The people along the sidewalk cheered and waved just as loudly as if you and the goat were General Lee and Traveller. Even the goat caught the merry infection of the festival time. He pranced as if he had good sense and ambitions. His goatee had a rakish cut and his lantern jaws vibrated like those of a saint entering the arena. It was even told that after certain super-duper parades some goats were satisfied with nothing less for supper than a battered sprinkling pot.

Spontaneous Shows

Many shows receive so much flagrant ballyhooing the actual performance is often a pitiful anti-climax. All too frequently the lavish build-up is an awkward club that beats the life out of the performance. By the sharpest of contrasts, the spontaneous shows of yesterday made up in verve what they may have lacked in aplomb.

These shows came to the small towns in slow, uneven trickles. They came just often enough to keep the public on its toes. And the show seemed always to come when no one expected it, when the town was three-fourths asleep or had its back completely turned. It may be fanciful, but you seem to remember that the show came on a particularly peevish afternoon, when a crow not only had to carry its rations but its entertainment, too. These shows, the dog and pony and monkey shows (and the human fly) came to town in hot weather, when traveling conditions were favorable.

On the summer afternoon the town was hot, lonely, dejected, and sticky as hell during a revival meeting. Everyone moved as if he were in a trance. If Jesse James had still been living he could have robbed the train passengers and toted off the railroad track, too. The moping hounds lying beneath the underpinning of the stores wouldn't have chased an arthritic rabbit that had a bucket of pot-likker and corn bread tied around its neck.

Then the show came in unexpectedly as stray thunder taps in mid-winter. No one ever remembered seeing the show get to town. It just happened, the way water boils or a clock hand moves. The showman (usually there was but one) went immediately to the coolest spot available, maybe to a muggy alley, or to a huge oak on the public square. If you didn't like the show, you not only didn't have to stay, you didn't have to come.

A lot of folks didn't have to leave their straw or electric fans. They looked out the windows of the stores and offices in which they worked. Some climbed trees. A few of the tree climbers thought this put them beyond range of the hat the showman passed to take up collection. Occasionally, there was the living embodiment of the story of Zaccheus, a small man who could not see above the shoulders of taller people. The first to gather were curious idlers, usually. But their laughter sifted through the sweaty toils of summer air and others came gradually. The adults stood or sat on the fenders of cars or in wagons. Many slouched against a brick wall or a tree. The children squatted in front of grown people, or made camels' humps of their fathers' shoulders.

Many shows were limited to a pony and a dog. The pony was "taught" or "teached," according to how high you went in school. He could count, by pawing, and he could answer questions the same way or by shaking his head. The dog was equally as brilliant. He was especially adept to striking all sorts of poses, playing dead, playing important, or being a naughty dog and hiding behind his forefeet. Together, pony and dog did gymnastics. The grand finale came when the dog rode the pony, all the while jumping through a hoop the showman held.

Then, again, amid summer's listless hopelessness, the old Italian slipped into town with his organ grinder and his little monkey. The Italian put his music box in front of the drug store. As he ground out frayed and chipped bits of Verdi or Rossini, the little monkey worked the crowd. He danced and bobbed or waved and doffed his little hat for coins. He climbed to the store and office windows to get the coins of the people lounging and smiling there. Above the strains of "La Traviata" the old Italian intoned: "Give uh da munk some mun, give uh du munk some mun, tank yu."

There was an elderly colored man who came to every Southern town once a year, continuously, from the time of Grover Cleveland to that of Warren Harding. Maybe, he covered the whole country. But once a year he came to town, and he never sold anything, nor passed a hat. For a fact, no one recalls that he ever said a word. Whence he came or went, no one ever knew. One minute, he was in the middle of town and the next minute he was a breathless blur. A lot of folks believed the old Negro materialized from some kind of funny joke and then vanished in a cloud, the same as Elisha.

He marched briskly down the main drag leading two whopping geese. These geese were bigger than any ever seen in town before or since. One was named George Green and the other

Jacob Fuller. If these geese had been children, they were big enough to do pig problems in arithmetic.

The venerable colored man had a sign on his back that advertised goose grease. The uses of goose grease, in those days, were more numerous than those of whiskey, turpentine, and liniment combined. The sign proclaimed the virtues of a particular brand of goose grease.

Since county seat towns were notoriously short, the parade was over almost before it began. George Green and Jacob Fuller were great white ships blown by a soundless wind. The local look-outs passed the word and the word swept the county with the absorbing tenacity of the honeysuckle vines. The next day, a farmer ten miles off would ask the mail man or some visitor from town: "Well, what's the news in the big city?"

"Nothing much specially but I'll tell you a fact. George Green and Jacob Fuller passed through yesterday afternoon."

The farmer slapped his thigh and went off to tell his wife and kids. The word "geese" was not mentioned. George Green and Jacob Fuller were vital personalities. They had been to town once more and the creeks and the trains could run henceforth without fear of molestation. Ten million details were tied in with these annual visits. Weddings, deaths, fires, and fortunes were not related to the calendar nearly so much as the annual visits of George Green and Jacob Fuller.

Occasionally, some evil man with a spiteful penchant for graphic detail would say that the originals were dead, that these were two brand new George Greens and Jacob Fullers. Grown men disputed testily. Some took off their coats and offered battle. Some quit speaking. Many an old boundary dispute was rehashed just because of the snide suggestions of the evil, forthright man. Children cried and turned on Santa Claus, George Washington, and the Sunday school teacher.

Parents, though, were quick with positive reassurances. It was a lie, a damnable lie. Why, anyone with the brains of a misbegotten mole knew these two geese were the same old George and Jacob. Why, you couldn't kill George Green and Jacob Fuller any quicker than you could carve down Stone Mountain with a fifty cent pocket knife.

Certain hobos doubled as animal showmen. You must remember the continental difference between the hobo and the bum or tramp. The hobo willingly did odd jobs or put on a show for his board and room. The miserable tramp never brought anything to town but his frightening appetite and his outrageous lies. He lied colossally, but not adroitly, to try to ingratiate himself in the soft hearts of gullible children. He lied about the places he had been and the people he knew in a clumsy effort to get the children to lead him to heaping hand-outs.

The tramp slept anywhere the dogs permitted, but the hobo was given a dry berth in a barn or out-building. Often, the hobo slept in the local jail. The hobo did odd jobs for jailers along the line, and he always was welcomed. He might work the jailer's garden or help the jailer's wife with household jobs. Frequently, an intelligent hobo helped the jailer's children with their lessons.

The really discerning hobo maneuvered his peregrinations so his overnight stops would coincide with the jails that served the best food. Normally, the jailer's wife did the cooking. Some of these women were heralded for their elegant stews, while others leaned more to beef or mutton. Some were rare bakers and still others were high priestesses in the mystical relationships between middling meat and ham-hock and fresh vegetables in a pot.

One enterprising hobo, popularly called the "Arkansas Traveler," was a rustic Duncan Hines. From him, the chosen fraternity learned subtle trade secrets about the food and accommodations at various jails.

The average jailer in the innocent era, always left at least one cell unlocked for the favored hobos. It might be sullying truth to say a candle was left in the window, but the bars seemed increasingly less formidable.

Some hobos, some itinerants, did tricks with animals, regardless of where they ate or stayed the night. The strolling performer had a trick bicycle that could be packed and carried almost as easily as a folding drinking cup. He was attended by one companion, a monkey or dog that rode the bicycle until it was broken down to one wheel. There were double-acts in which the hobo and the dog or monkey did dexterous feats on the bicycle simultaneously.

Others had trained crows that counted or answered questions along the lines of the "teached" pony. This trouper reached in one pocket and pulled out a compressed top hat. From the other pocket he pulled out his precious crow. And infrequently, a hobo with a car brought a boxing bear to town. The impresario offered a flat sum, say $25.00, to any local man who would stay three rounds with the bear. A ring was put on the stage of the local theater or opera house. Since defeating a bear was a questionable feat for a sane man, often it was a drunk who volunteered to try to win the cash prize. Audacity dissolved once the gladiator was in the ring. A bear, even one outfitted in boxing gloves, is never comical at close range. As a rule, the challenger was spent from the exhaustion of running long before the third round came around.

These tiffs were the forerunners of slap-stick comedy. Mayhem hardly ever occurred. Ever and anon, some enterprising idiot would secrete pepper and sling it in the bear's face. The challenger wound up about ten rows out in the audience, still devoid of $25.00 to pay on his broken ribs.

Well, in the aloof light of clinical detachment, maybe these weren't much shows, but as Teddy Roosevelt said about the Spanish-American War, is was the only one going on at the time. Its value lay within its spontaneity. Many a steaming afternoon that had been rued was saved from despair and oblivion. All the spontaneous shows had elements of success except the trained fleas.

There was always one man in the crowd who said he had a cousin out West who died from typhus caught at a trained flea show. Not everyone believed this story but few were willing to gamble. However, come to think about it, even the abortive flea show did some lasting good. People talked about the possibilities of typhus for a few days and not so much of dying from heat prostration or the summer complaint.

A Dozen, Cousin Bees

Honey is the most universally popular of all terms of endearment. (I dismiss "dear" because it doesn't imply anything and is actually a utility salutation. I ignore "darling" because it is still a little too pretentious for lawyers, football coaches, and farmers. Aside from the anemic rococo grandeur when darling is used by show folks, it is used by ordinary folks mostly when a wife is angry at her husband or when a woman hopes to get tapped for a literary club or when she is doling out largesse to the solicitor for the underprivileged.)

The married lovers who say honey at least twice in every sentence evidently think about melted honey, if they think about it at all. They probably don't see honey as being in the comb. Honey, as jammed into the comb, forms a rough picture and the wax sticks all over your teeth if you eat smack out of the box or frame. These lovers who send "honey" dancing out brightly as the evening star certainly don't think about bees. And the lovers who detest the group mind, the individuals who say "honey bee," may have been stung by a chigger but probably not by an irate bee.

Actually, few folks today have any conversance with bees. We talk about bees as we talk about atomic submarines, by dint of monumental volumes of hearsay, not from close sight or any touch at all. The whole business is absurd. Whereas, "honey" is essential to marital conversation, the bee hive, about to bust on your head, is strictly an ingredient of a nightmare. Despite all the saccharine yammering and the fear of stings, bee today is pretty much a figure of speech. It's a long way from the wife's: "Don't be so stupid, honey," to the place where bees are kept.

Bees are intelligent but not brilliant. The average bee's intelligence is somewhere between that of a smart educated sheep and a second-rate man. Bees hate doleful, despondent people and they sting them at every opportunity. In the horse and buggy era, country bees did their best to disperse mourners at funerals. Bees can't stand crying on a lovely day. They used to lie in wait and buzz-bomb funerals. There weren't enough bees to go around, and news was slow, but with the material they had, the bees made it rough on mourners. Back when black veils were worn, bees attacked few grieving widows. It was no use in wasting a stinger, and, candidly, bees do observe some amenities. However, to be ultra candid, there were times when a peevish or perverse bee infiltrated a black veil. This snide attack was perpetrated only after the attacking bee had ascertained positively that the woman behind the veil was putting on an act. Often the recipient was an aspiring legatee whose claim was based more on wishful histrionics than probate actualities. The attack had two salutary effects. A palpable fraud was unveiled and an interminable series of orations was terminated.

After the disuse of the veil and the advent of closed automobiles bees concentrated more on front porches. The motivation was still the dissipation of gloom but each inertia-laced summer day saw some gross mistakes. Bees frequently hit porch nappers who were not despondent but lethargic. It is entirely possible that bees, smart as most are, misunderstood the mission of the porch in insular America. In the endless stupor of the afternoon, when the pots and pans on the sky-stove rattled with boiling fury, remarkable spiritual equipoise paraded as baleful scowling. The bees not only came to the porch to castigate and elevate, they took partial seasonal quarters in porch columns. If not smoked out soon enough, the bees could make the column definitely hazardous. Either way the bees had done their full best to dispel apathy passing as grumpiness. If the stingers didn't revitalize the vacuous old piazza, the smoke galvanized everyone into frenetic action.

The standard remedy for a bee sting was the immediate application of wet tobacco. This anodyne is changeless and is always effective. If the American Medical Journal has not yet taken official cognizance of the fact, it is well known that bee stings are much more serious in cotton sections and among sects that frown on tobacco. When the bees stung back yonder, you put some pipe or sack tobacco in your lip and stuck the lump on the affected place. If a child got stung, the Papa rolled some loose tobacco on his tongue and stuck it on the sting.

However, Papas in better homes were never allowed to take

a chew from a plug for this purpose, not even a tiny chew. Women considered pipe or sack tobacco sanitary. This may be due to all the pictures of Sir Walter Raleigh sucking the clay pipe. Even when loose tobacco was moisted with the tongue for medical applications, it still passed the women's sanitary tests. Chewing was frightfully unsanitary. The unsavory connotation was not ameliorated just because certain eminent political leaders, bankers, and ball players were rabid chewers.

Besides, rich folks had the grace and brains to chew in private. Common folks splattered the front lawn, to say nothing of the front porch banisters. Too, much chewing tobacco could be picked up free. For instance, throughout the entire tobacco belt you could pick up loose leaves around the auction warehouses. Additionally, everyone knew that pipe and sack tobacco denoted social and economic status. Wasn't it known around the globe that Alfred, Queen Victoria's precious and gentle Lord Tennyson, smoked Bull Durham? Even when a rich man chewed an expensive plug, his wife was eternally terrified for fear someone would think he mooched the stuff at an auction warehouse or got it as a premium for buying buggy robes or horse collars.

For example, some years ago, a visitor at the Governor's Mansion in Raleigh, N. C., was stung while sitting on the piazza. The governor was inside the mansion with a full jaw of costly store-bought stuff but his wife made him spit out his quid and run to a store three blocks away for a sack of Bull Durham. The breathless chief executive lipped up a ball of curative and smacked it on the guest's wrist, and the threat of serious poison was precluded as the integrity and dignity of exalted office were saved from the cuspidor.

Make no mistake. Wet tobacco is the best medicine for a bee sting. If you don't think it will work, just stick a finger in a hive. There used to be a fairly common belief that these curative properties of loose tobacco were advanced by James Buchanan Duke. (Or was it his father, Washington Duke? I don't think it was R. J. Reynolds, Sr., whose naturalistic interests were more on camels than bees.) A lot of people thought this was inordinately thoughtful of Mr. Duke. A few pettifoggers said Mr. Duke was just trying to sell more tobacco. Naturally, some would say that. Today, the cigarette folks don't say much about it, one way or the other. Even if a filter does nothing for a bee sting, the rest of the cigarette works as satisfactorily as the old sack stuff did. (There ought to be at least one vagrant buzzer somewhere in all this immense amount of green fields, rolling pastures, bridle paths, golf courses, and assorted rustic scenery you see in the cigarette ads. Maybe, just maybe, some filter-tipped cutie will get stung smack in the foot. It would be terrible if they have to send to another network to get some pipe tobacco or snuff—I mean, of course, through sheer and prissy ignorance of what the tailor-made job can do.)

Anent the abject loathing of the funeral, older readers will recall, possibly, the tender old custom of "telling the bees." The modern may call it a naive and primitive superstition but "telling the bees" was a serious ritual. When a member of a human family died, a member of the family that kept bees, the hives were dressed in black crepe. It was believed the bees would desert these swarms and seek new ones if they were not informed of the death. Someone "told the bees" and the black crepe was left on the hives for a reasonable period of general mourning. "Telling" was a sing-song, low chant. A neighbor or friend of the bereaved family walked about the swarms sing-songing the news.

There are countless tales of unexpected returnees observing the ritual. In many of the ancient stories, a lover had come for his bride. Laden with the fortune he had gone to seek, he stopped his horse on a hill that overlooked his betrothed's home. With agonizing suddenness he saw someone telling the bees. Was it his lady love, or was it an older member of the household?

Since suffering and tragedy are essentials of drama, it was usually his love who was lost. In some of the dramas, the horseman came a little closer. A look from the teller of the bees conveyed the stark tragedy. Most of the time, the crushed returnee rode off and was never seen again. Now and again, he whipped and spurred the horse and dropped the reins. The horse carried him to his death along the large crevice, the big hedge, the high fence, the roaring rapids.

The pathetic saga of the neighborhood suitor was incorporated into future bee telling. Usually a girl was chosen to tell the bees, probably because of the softness of the voice, the assuaging elements of humming communication. The girl walked in and out of the swarms, singing the terrible announcement and placing the black crepe. John Greenleaf Whittier left behind such a poetic account. Perhaps, New Englanders didn't go in for gore or for lovers vanished forever. The man in Whittier's poem has come to call, after a month's absence. He sees a girl "telling" and he assumes his sweetheart's elderly grandfather has died. Alas, it is his beloved Mary. Whittier didn't throw in the dramatic epilogue so cherished by Southerners. But he did leave, as conclusion, this fine stanza:

> "And the song she was singing ever since
> In my ear sounds on:—
> 'Stay at home, pretty bees, fly not hence.
> Mistress Mary is dead and gone.' "

The modern, flippant and calloused as to the niceties of tradition, will likely say these old families must have been stringently pushed for company if they went to all the trouble to sing to bees to keep swarms from roving. In fact, Lloyd Bell, a South Carolina legislator, recently introduced a bill to protect his constituents from "Yankee bees" that escape from out-of-state vehicles. Frankly, this bill isn't so hot. Any man who drives through South Carolina with a swarm of bees for traveling companions certainly should be immune to any kind of arrest. There are friendly pythons and docile alligators but bees hardly ever qualify for gentility. Too, the natural assumption is that some of these bee-letters are headed for Florida. That commonwealth, according to the folders, is a land of gay indolence and opulence. It may be a land of milk but it obviously isn't honey.

Generally speaking, though, bees are not much of a problem today. The public's touch has disintegrated since the demise of the opened-carriage funeral and the decline of the front porch. In twenty years kids will not know whether honey comes from cows or a test tube. The kid will assume "honey" is a family name. His mother was named Fannie Honey before she became Frances H. Entwhistle. The kid's father calls her honey so she will remember how tricks were at the old homestead before she came to gleaming suburbia.

The Animals Preempt the Square

In summer, almost all the small towns shut down at one p.m. on Wednesdays for the half-holiday. For all the intents and purposes of the endless afternoon of unutterable lethargy, the business men lock their doors and throw away the keys.

The courthouse square and the principal business section are gripped by the stark desertion that permeates the movie set of the mildewed ghost town. The merciless sun scowls straight down, flailing the peevish streets with searing fists that hold red-hot railroad spikes. It is almost as if the sun is trying to eradicate the place because everyone ran off and left him to fester and blister alone and unaided. The uptown section is an anvil on which the sun hammers and beats his furious spite.

The fountain on the courthouse lawn gurgles the way a madman gets his tremulous breath. It sails higher than ever. The white spume is a great eel dancing angrily in the maddening light of the sun. Then it is a sullen worm groveling low to pout and fret and to utter tempestuous imprecations about gross inattention. After an interval of supine sulking, the fountain is an enormous white cat arching her majestic back to leap almost on top of the courthouse.

The fountain spends itself in poetic anguish and crashes as if pierced by an arrow. It changes form and flutters out tantalizing as a bird on a silver string. From the way the bird picks and pecks you'd almost believe it is bobbing for a golden apple.

But, save for one man, perhaps, this show goes without observation, and this human abandonment has created in the fountain the same gnawing rancor that afflicts the sun.

You half-expect the Confederate soldier on the marble monument to put down his gun and wipe his brow and walk across the square and drink from the fountain. A stranger from outer space would flee from the vacuous face of such scorching desolation and insolence. If it weren't for the few animals around, this stranger would assume fall-out from radiation had foreclosed on the town permanently.

A few animals keep watch in the same furtive manner a beached sailor might scan a sea long swept of all naval and human traffic. The town mutt lies under the wooden steps of the back of a store. The front of the store, on a main street, has a touch of Fifth Avenue. The rear of the store falls on its hind-parts in an alley. The town mutt hugs the dankness under the steps so tightly you know he wouldn't bark if all the chicken bones in the whole county were piled at his feet.

From the misery of his panting you would believe he is the most unredeemed sinner of the age trying to get the breath to ask forgiveness. His face asks all the foolish questions an idiot might put in broken English to a French scholar. His eyes are rimmed with sweat and mucus and his nose is an over-ripe piece of apple some man cut out and threw away. But his tail beats and tap-taps with the rapid regularity of a telegraph instrument in full service. This tail-message isn't restricted to ten words; for, during the time from one p.m. to sundown the town mutt will click-clack, flam-flam a billion dots and dashes that are incomprehensible to all save himself.

What he is tattooing so rapidly but uninspiringly is nothing more than a way of whistling in the heat jungle. The town mutt thinks he's being cremated and he wags his tail against the concrete of the alley floor to let his head understand his back parts are not electrocuted. It's too hot to sleep and if he dozes momentarily he awakens from a nightmare. The shadow makes the rain-barrel a gorilla come to chew him alive. The tail-thumping, then, may be just a device to stave off the brief attacks of fear.

Stuck in the hard jaw of the courthouse is a clock. On the summer Wednesday afternoon it takes this clock about six months to run the hand from two p.m. to half-past. This cumbersome trip is tortuously slow despite the fact it is a down-hill journey all the way. The clock sullenly collects its sizzling strength to clap its hands twice for two p.m. This is done the way an irate housewife might ring a bell twice to summon someone she doesn't like to eat a meal she didn't want to prepare, and which she burned.

The way the clock's hand tours down to half-past two, you would think it is a mountain climber with a broken leg coming down from the peak. There are supposed to be five minutes between each numeral but at least four of these minutes have slipped off to the deep woods to take a prolonged snooze. A series of pigeons seems to be flying toward the deep woods. Maybe, the clock is sending these relay teams to drag the truant minutes back to the square, to their jobs between the numerals.

Even as the clock appears to emulate a drunk man with his peg-leg caught in a hole on a bridge, wandering eternally to nowhere, a "residential" poodle comes up the street to the square. He has slipped away from home. This is obvious from the jaunty way he bounces, from the curiosity that marks every stride. This rash young thing has more inquisitive innocence than weather judgment. Likely, he ran away while his master has gone fishing or is locked in with a fan.

He's come up town to see the sights. If he had the Delphic wisdom of that old pro, the town mutt, he would stay in his own cool, dainty parlor. But this is his first adventure alone. He has never seen the square save from a car window. This burning desolation is to him what creation must have been to the first observer. So, he'll see it all, revel in it all, chew it down, and swallow it to keep him going when his protectors have him inundated in the parlor again.

Freedom is such ecstasy he seems oblivious of the fact that he's prancing in a furnace. He paces in front of a haberdashery, glides up and down in front of the window displays as if trying to decide between sports jacket and slacks or the brown dacron suit.

The dime store window has all the treasures, jewels, and fabulous oddments in creation. This pooch, free from the coddling lap, is blinded by the avalanche of sterling rarities. The dime store window represents a world of make-believe. It's a fairyland or some mirage produced by charred minds. The puppydog bounces to the curbing and wheels suddenly to see if the wonderland evaporated while his eyes were turned. He laughs and can almost be heard as he tells the ineffable trinkets not to run away or to get into any mischief as he leaves for further exploration.

He canters briskly across the pavement, the hot street making him sling his feet militantly as a guardsman. He stands in silent bumfuzzlement in front of the blunt, bluff immensity of the courthouse. He stretches his neck slowly up, photographing the facade brick by brick, on to the sluggish clock, and finally to the belltower, itself. He is akin to a lone man standing in the bottom of a vast rock quarry trying to see the earth beyond the rim.

Near the entrance to the courthouse is a big bulletin board on which is published a short current history of the county in all sorts of legal notices—foreclosure sales, notices of administration, jury lists, livestock sales and sales of household and kitchen furniture, "wanted" posters, liens, and condemnations.

At first you think this doggie's trying to pick up a fast buck on the forced sale of some farm land. You wouldn't be surprised to hear him ask if there is any tobacco allotment on the farm that's advertised for public sale. Then you realize it is the "wanted" posters he finds so intriguing. One thing's sure: He's no bounty hunter, not this happy pup. If one of these alleged villains stepped down from the bulletin board this doggie would be back in his cool parlor in three jerks, even if he had to slide down the chimney to get into the house.

This dog sees a strange breed plastered on the board. The people he knows don't have numbers printed across their shirt fronts. He looks for the lady who feeds him dog food and for the little boy who wrestles with him on the rug, at the foot of whose bed he sleeps in a fancy basket. But mistress and youthful master must be unknown in this endless brick canyon. They belong to another world, a clean, cool, orderly one, and he backs from the front of the courthouse and darts around the side of the building.

There is a miniature garden on the courthouse lawn, to one side of the building, that is planted and kept by the garden club. This plot is so orderly, is so neatly fragrant, it seems to have more in common with a floral design for a flower show than with actual nature. In the middle is a little pool in which all sorts of exotic fishes frolic and shuttle. The dog sits on his haunches and peers into the water. He bounces back two yards when his wrinkled picture flashes back from the water. He edges up again, a cautious soldier on patrol. His wild eyes cast downward again and the miraculous portrait is still there.

He has found a home, a dwelling place, for an interval, anyhow. The favored puppy is now the boy taking his first glimpse at the garbled mirrors in a fun-house at a resort carnival. This water picture business is something no mortal or fellow member of his own lodge ever mentioned to him. If you study him with musing eyes you think of the legend of Narcissus. If the mischief gets the wind up, you think of the envious bulldog on the bank and the bullfrog in the pool.

According to the hoary song, one largely home-made, a dog came to a pool. The fish swam away from his reflection (or perhaps really from him) but the bullfrog sat with stolid stupidity gazing straight back at the dog. The graceful fish were too pretty to cuss, and the dog tried to think of some suitable invective for the unmovable frog. Just as the human does when he is angry and can't think of anything appropriate to say, this dog swore at the bullfrog, using such impotent banality as "fool":

"O, the bulldog on the bank,
And the bullfrog in the pool,
The bulldog called the bullfrog,
'You green old water fool.' "

And here in the middle of Wednesday afternoon's charcoal grill is the pool with the green-eyed dragon in the middle. But this is a fraudulent dragon that is as idly captivated by the pooch as the dog is with him. The frog sits in the middle like an inexpertly made May Pole. The silver and golden fish swim around the pole, listlessly. These fish get more hand-outs each day than the repenting bum gets at Christmas time. They stay in motion around the horny-headed pole but they are too glutted and gutted to strike at the fanciest lure ever devised.

Off the courthouse square, the vacuous immobility of Main Street is punctuated with a stop-light. Amid all the dreary stagnation of Wednesday afternoon, this traffic signal is a lightning bug blinking and flashing in an enormous desert. For all the practical purposes of the afternoon, it is a lighthouse stationed years beyond the sound of any ship's whistle.

The four faces of the stop-light are littered with bugs and various aerial insects. Most of these hangers-on are flies. Theirs is not the spirited, disputatious cacophony of the night-time assault on a naked light bulb suspended on a cord. These flies and bugs remind you of shipwreck victims clinging to any floatable debris handy. The noise is a whizzing sing-song, a mechanical sort of lamentation, but it lacks the morbid poignance of a dirge. This stop-light must be some kind of crude haven, but one devoid of charm and tenderness. The light is a place flies come to for the same reasons that half-panicked humans

assemble at a specific location when following the loose and garbled ends of a wild rumor. No fly, in all possibility, gives cre-
dence to the stop-light's being a refuge from the pitiless scorn
of Wednesday's nakedness. As is the usual procedure with
humans, when something untoward develops, one or two hap-
pen upon a location. This location, after loquacious excitement
is firmly stamped, is seen by scores of others as representing
some kind of haven. The essence, though, lies in proximity or
availability rather than natural attractiveness.

The four faces of the light will not accommodate all the restive horde. There is the same pushing and shoving that attends
the tremulous exit of a theater crowd. Some flies that can't
squeeze aboard fly around and around the light, and the lone
observer thinks of the Indians on their sleek ponies riding
around the circle of covered wagons. Finally, it is evident that
the hot faces don't inspire tenacity. Flies break off and their
places are filled quickly by new ones. It is almost as if some
insect divine were solemnly intoning: As these retire, let others
come.

Fifty yards from the light, away from the luminous shadows
of the courthouse, is the big "time" store. The enormous show
window has the fuzzy transparence of scotch tape. One tremendous fly tries with neurotic desperation to penetrate the
murky window glass. The buzzing of this one fly seems louder
than the blasts of the fire-horn at twelve noon on Saturday when
the rattle and din of men and machinery are rolling sound
waves. This lone fly, palpably mad from heat or thirst, storms
about the smudgy glass like a lone fighter pilot trying to van-
quish all the enemy ships from a vast, still sea.

From a slightly different vantage, this insanely angry fly gives
the impression of being trapped in some narrow cave or sub-
terranean passage. If he so thinks, he has realized no help is near

and that he must extricate himself by main strength and frenetic digging. The blinding sun must convince him all is darkness outside the pane. Light and hope are inside the "time"
store. The armed hand of man is not the enemy but a killing
portion of the self-same source that gave existence to the
temporarily demented whizzer.

Inside, the store cat sprawls on a pile of grain sacks. This mer-
cantile anachronism has abdicated any of the watchman duties
that may yet devolve upon store cats. In her sleep her trance-
like breathing comes with the methodical puffs of an oxygen
bag in an operating room. It is more akin to simulation than to
actual breathing. She's a fat rubber ball in which the rush of
air alternately is pumped in and expelled. If she rolled onto a
sharp nail the flood of air would rush all over the "time" store
with the force of a giant balloon spewing and squeaking out the
small, open end, the blowing end.

This store holds some of everything, including a kitchen sink.
With one hand a customer can pick up nuts and bolts while the
other hand reaches for cheese or perfume. In the middle of
1960's ruffled conformity, this store is a combination of all the
pictures, stories, and notions of all the general stores. The man
who first operated this store has been dead 100 years, but he
kept a cat here. So does the present owner. The cat comes with
the sense of operation. Some cat has been tied in profit and loss
every day of the store's existence.

Long ago, efficiency experts advocated that all cats in all sugar
barrels must go. The cat is inconsistent with modern merchan-
dising. But "time" store operators need only a stock of goods,
intricate knowledge of the community and its mores and personalities, and a bookkeeper who can figure mark-ups, interest
payments, and carrying charges. The cat came in with the first
barrel of molasses. The original cat and the first barrel rot and

rust in limbo, but this Wednesday afternoon another molasses barrel is only twenty paces from the sleeping cat.

This cat is one of the surviving royal potentates. She has the run of this building to a degree no President's wife has been extended in the White House. An interloping rat is no more exciting than the pan of milk. She eats when she's hungry, rests when she's tired, and she chooses her companions as rigorously as did King Arthur.

There are about 30,000 people in this county. Most of the male adults come into this building at some time during the year. Many come daily. This cat knows those who wander in and out far more intimately than the tax collector knows most of the folks with whom he deals. She offers no excuses for dislikes, and she can't be diverted by any succulent bribe. The haughtiest of prima donnas, she'd as soon snip at the banker's trousers as at those of the seediest transient.

One minute she's checking the cash register and the next she's supervising the weighing, bagging, and tying of fifty pounds of crimson clover. When the management holds a fish fry behind the store she pussy-foots around the spluttering pans and the table with the liquor and the ice water as imperially as a high-priced and especially meticulous caterer. No plate is set for her at the long table but her place is designated as distinctly as that of the Congressman when he's in town for a visit and a bait of fried fish.

She's ridden the fertilizer truck to virtually every farm in the county. When she meets the ice man you think he will ask her what size chunk is needed today. When the store truck is being loaded with farming equipment, she waits at the door in the cab to ride beside the driver. When sacks of grain are being loaded, she waits at the tail-gate to leap atop the load and to view the countryside from her regal perch on top. If she had a pair of long white gloves she would already have served a term as president of the local Woman's Club.

Wednesday afternoon, though half snail and half turtle, does manage to stay in bumpy caterpillar motion. The fattest, slowest, laziest thing on earth would have to move if the devil had a blowtorch jammed against his tail. And Wednesday crawls on two sore knees towards the shank of the afternoon. In the distance some comatose crows barely wheel on sagging wings. The sun is so devastatingly bright and sharp there is the blurred illusion of mist. The sheen of these laconic crows seems lacklustre as a bleached stick. These crows are suspended in midair, in some misty realm that intersperses the town and the deep woods. They must be some kind of skirmishers that have come out on indifferent pickets to determine conditions in this town. Is it still unoccupied? Can the other birds sweep in from the forests and sport upon the courthouse lawn without fear of molestation by din or menacing footfalls? Ordinarily, these visitors preempt the courthouse square just at the hour businessmen give commerce to the faint suggestion of stars. But Wednesday must cause consternation all the way from the banks of the garrulous creek to the top of the highest pine tree and on to the end of the longest rail fence.

By now the clock in the face of the courthouse is running faster. Probably, this shift ends at six o'clock, and many a writhing workman picks up renewed energy when the arduous trek is about done. The brakes are thrown away and the hand is a wheel, a magic hoop racing down the slick hill that goes from five to five-thirty. It is hard for the lone observer not to recall the ancient lesson in the primer about the little engine that said: "I think I can. I know I can. I know I can."

The square is still empty. It's too soon for picnickers, swimmers, boating parties, and fishermen to come home, and it isn't late enough for the house-bound folks to take a joy ride, a spin-around for fresh air and sights. But there is a suggestion of twilight. The sun hasn't shot his wad. He still has ammunition in his coat pockets. But time is spoiling his aim, or perhaps, as insatiably gluttonous as he is, he thinks he's done enough damage for one afternoon. He fires broken salvos. Some hit the target, some are near misses, and a lot are going over, passing harmlessly beyond.

The air holds no balm, no refreshment or sustenance. But there is a change. The air was a piece of chalk a little while ago. It has not yet changed to a soaking, sustaining compress but it has a little of the moisture of a leaf.

In the back alley, the town mutt gets up the slow, tedious way a heavy door opens when you have to push hard against it. He stretches and yawns and creaks like a rusty wagon. The post office is his next stop. Every afternoon but Wednesday and Sunday he meets a hundred or more folks here. He doesn't pick up any cash or rations at the post office but he gets a lot of affection, good will, and advice. He comes from the alley, his legs grinding and screeching like those of the ramshackle wagon.

Between the alley and the square there is an old harness shop that now sells assorted hardware, sporting equipment, and electrical supplies. In the window is a hobby horse, an unasked for legacy from the patient, strong men who once fashioned leather into bridles and saddles. Each afternoon the town mutt stops before the hobby horse. This horse must have been foaled the year Stephen Foster wrote "The Camptown Races." Boys who once rode him to Gettysburg and on the quest with Galahad now have middle-aged grandsons. The town mutt sees this hobby horse every afternoon at post office time, but he still must think the steed is going somewhere.

You can hear the town mutt thinking: "Well, he's still here. Maybe he'll be galloping tomorrow. Otherwise, what's the need of standing up all day long?" If the town mutt is in any wise conversant with military parlance he is probably mumbling: "Don't ever call your soldier to attention unless you are going to drill him."

This horse has been at attention, though, since the local military company left town for the Spanish-American War. The snows of winter and the suns of summer have not decreased his stature one cubit. At the demise of the harness shop, the cobwebs were torn away, and he is as young in appearance as he was in Woodrow Wilson's era. There is every reason to suspect he will survive any H-Bomb wars and be around to show the new model cave-kids a tangible slice of the animal fair of the quaint days when only the birds flew in the skies.

The town mutt shakes out some of his kinks and saunters on towards the square. The lone observer is not visible to him. The mutt sniffs the grass of the lawn as if hunting for something he lost this morning. He cocks one leg, making a three-legged stool on the lawn, and quickly puts it down. But local desolation puts the imps of mischief in his mind. He slips up on the stone steps that lead into the courthouse. He takes a hasty survey of the square, cocks his right hind leg, officially this time, and leaves a puddle as some sort of friendly "go to hell" calling card. He goes buckity-buckity down towards the post office, dragging behind in a sort of movie fade-out shot, the retreating waves and shadows of the tag-end of Wednesday afternoon, on a summer day in a little Southern town.

Cock-of-the-Walk

On a May morning, the biggest thing in the state of North Carolina is not Mt. Mitchell, nor are the volcanic waves off Hatteras the most powerful force. The biggest and the most powerful entity in the entire state is the barnyard rooster. (The rooster may be equally as portentous in other commonwealths but I can speak with certainty only of North Carolina.) When he struts and preens his feathery finery and flaunts his fiery comb he is informing the world it couldn't possibly start this day without his strident blessings.

He pours out his blessings in brittle bursts of graveled crowings, but this call to action contains intimations of admonitions. He struts and crows to let you know he owns this earth in fee simple, that he will deed it over shortly to mankind, but his guttural exhortations entail a stern trust: You must handle this day carefully, suck it down to the last drops of sweetness. For after all, this rooster is saying that he got this day together from fragments of nocturnal clouds and mists. When he brandished his tail feathers and called down the light with militant monody, mankind was yet snoring and had no knowledge of the cock's frenzied labors nor any hand in their success.

The sounds of the day begin with the tiny salvos of plates and pans being rattled, of doors being slammed, of engines being raced. The swashbuckling cock-of-the-walk is forgotten and unheard by the time the morning slides into second gear. The old swaggerer is obsolete by nine a.m. The cock-of-the-earlier-walk gets his consolation from a chat with the little gray hen. He tells her that she may know him only as a Don Juan but in all reality he is the boy who unscrambled this day and put it into silver motion.

It may be superfluous, but to stay in touch with actuality, it must be conceded that roosters aren't prevalent today. If they are more numerous than conditions indicate, their incredible virility must be well secreted. There are roosters on farms, of course, and a few are scattered around in small towns. But the mighty cock's mission as morning clarion, as time in form of tocsin, ended with the accelerated urbanization of small towns, when chickens and cows and vegetable gardens became small-townish in small towns.

The people who write poems, jingles, picture books, and assorted animal stories for children usually have side-stepped the bombastic cock. A mental block may have been caused by the sadistic rituals of cock-fighting. Literary revulsion may have been prompted by the sorry spectacle of men devoid of the brains to entertain themselves putting down good money for the outrageously distorted thrill of seeing irate animals kill each other in furious flashes of crimson. Or, perhaps, some block was incident to the rooster's legendary role as seducer and traducer. The rooster is depicted as the one creature that never had enough hours in which to express his physical enthusiasm. The laureates of the little people probably saw the cock as untoward or unseemly in juxtaposition to the superficial purity that is associated with unfurrowed brows.

Simultaneously, the hen has been enthroned on fluffy pillows and to this hour is clucked over, mothered and swaddled with dulcet words on metaphorical nests. Unfortunately, most of the females of the species are highly susceptible to early death by decapitation or hit and run drivers. Conversely, the rooster's saga is a paean to survival. The rooster is to barnyard culture what advertising is to television. You may not admire either one but replacement is a formidable chore. There are retired roosters who are probably drawing Social Security benefits or annuities from laying mash dealers or chicken pot pie wholesalers. Aside from old age, or too much attention to duty by an over-zealous and foolish beginner, the only other primary cause of death was the church sociable.

Chicken salad was standard fare. Nay more, in many places it was almost spiritually mandatory. Chicken salad was made from roosters. Chicken salad was synonymous with the church supper, church circle, and missionary society meetings. (The dish was served at most of the small town wedding receptions but it wasn't precisely mandatory.) Some women said hens were too sweet and juicy to be sacrificed for chicken salad. There was also the fear that a productive layer might be slaughtered.

So, the rooster became the Nathan Hale of the piece. A lot of women hated roosters because of their relentless aggressive attack on women chickens. The women realized these sorties were essential, but after all, my dear, there it was in broad open daylight without the protective screening of a bush. The bravado of the cock reminded the lady of her husband's smutty jokes. Often, in a consummate fit of chagrin, a woman would kill a rooster and then have to invite the sisters for an unscheduled meeting.

Naturally, impotent fowls were quickly consigned to the banquet spread. This determination was really beyond the ken of many housewives but any bird with drooping tail feathers was in the pot before he could present contrary evidence to the court. A truth even more luminous was that most folks secretly believed it didn't matter much what kind of meat went into the chicken salad. The meat was soggily camouflaged with diced celery, almonds, cooked dressing, and mayonnaise. It usually wore a topcoat of cucumber pickles and soda crackers or saltines. The ignominy of it all was that the gallant rooster that had con-tributed his last ounce of strength to the cause had died as vainly as the soldier who gets killed a few minutes after a foolish war has officially ended, has already been declared lost.

Of course, as everyone knows, chicken salad was relegated to the ash can when the snack bar came in and churches went into the restaurant and catering business in such a way as to vex local professional purveyors of hot and cold food.

Maybe it's the widespread influence of Dr. Kinsey's reports but today the cock-of-the-walk is encouraged in his strides toward longevity. Inquisitive pilgrims from the city seek him out as feverishly as they search for arrowheads, battered warming pans, ante-bellum andirons, tea pots, corner cupboards, and other priceless objects of rustic art. A few even bring cracked corn. They scatter this cracked corn with the grandiloquent largesse they bestow nuts on the monkeys in the cage. But you can't tell how this combination of belated adulation and curiosity affects the rooster. He stands as stolidly and austerely as a Prussian Guard. He may be soaking up all this attention, vicariously, for his badly tarnished grandsires or he might be sustained by the thought that one of these grinning idiots will toss him a lissome pullet instead of the cracked corn.

The old rooster may be antiquated in the atomic age, but he still cries the glory of the May day as fervently as if the President were listening. These ebullient sounds, bred of inherent brashness, part the last folds of semi-darkness and usher in the day just as if a curtain were being lifted on a darkened stage. The rooster's crow is a flailing maul that splits the fact of daylight as if it were a sharp ax on pine wood. When the morning shows signs of being late for work the rooster still blows his cornet as if the crescendo is a threat to dock the day's pay. It's really heart-warming to know that a few feathered alarm clocks are still around, to think of the proud face flashing brightly as if it were the morning's coat of arms.

The Animal as Cupid's Agent

Animals used to be integral in courtship. To be blunt and rather trite, many of us who are complaining about taxes and living costs would be permanently absolved of all complaints if it hadn't been for some animal. Many a perishing romance was rescued for posterity by dint of a noble or fractious animal.

The dog that had to be walked saved a lot of love affairs from a lot of rock piles. In fact, many an oppressed swain made his lady love a present of a lap or house dog that required regular constitutionals. In the exalted era of the parlor, the swain saw more of his girl's father, mother, sisters, brothers, uncles, and aunts and less of fair Maggie. Only the really resolute could outwait, outsit, the horde of relatives.

The first two hours the parlor traffic was more dense than the butcher shop's on Saturday night. The older relatives played rook or read newspapers when they were not slyly and snidely interrogating the courtier about his finances and future prospects, to say nothing of his religious and political affiliations and any possible predilections for pool halls or tent shows. The girl's younger brothers and sisters dumped homework in the boy's lap, when they weren't kicking his shins and sticking pencils in his neck.

But the boy endured with the grim perseverance with which the Old Guard Republicans sweated out FDR's four elections. When the last officious idiot blundered to bed, when hollering distance with the girl was reduced to tempestuous fingertouch, some blatherskite came back for a dose of soda. And if the night was as unsullied as a cherub's breath, some crank came downstairs to check the windows against possible storms. All the rapacious little brothers and sisters had to be watered. Some knotty headed kid fell over a chair and the whole confounded household was aroused. The dining room and parlor by now resembled a National Democratic Convention. Old Aunt Gert had a stomach ache. She got some milk and everyone else decided he might come down with a gastric disorder, too. An impromptu feast was put on the dining room table.

Obviously, the wings of the two doves could not sustain such a load. Love can't fly with a lunatic asylum on each shoulder. But, the dog, that imperishable combination of Socrates and Eros, had come in at the dramatic moment.

He had to be walked at least once and often twice during the evening. The boy held the leash with one hand and hugged and caressed with the other hand. If Yogi Berra were as unbelievably dexterous with two hands as this boy was with one hand, why old Yogi could catch every pitcher in the American League simultaneously while boning up on "Swan's Way" and posing for a toothpaste ad.

(And here's a delicate secret many boy lovers didn't learn until they were long married and their own sons were courting: Fair Maggie watered the lap dog copiously during the later afternoon and early evening. Whatever else might afflict this poodle, his kidneys were never retarded as to action. The girl, flesh and mind, was purer than snow that can be seen only from a jet plane and not clearly from this vantage.

Hubert Entwhistle, doubling as Lochinvar, could think of Dulcet Maggie having kidneys and unmentionable inner organs about as readily as Queen Victoria could think of Prince Albert's organizing the Sinn Fein. There was nothing between her mouth and her toes but her heart. If he had suspected this paragon watered the pooch, someone would have had to lead him around the block, and pretty damned quickly, too.)

The cat was helpful but too erratic to be counted upon strongly in a pinch. A cat, properly trained, could be sicked on some non-existent enemy down the street. In fact, in warm weather when the front porch swing was the Garden of Eden, some sharp boy lovers tossed toy rats down the shaded lanes. Once in action, the cat was not suitably tractable. She climbed trees that would baffle General Pike and she crawled under houses. The cat got the lovers away from the house but it didn't decrease much of the normal elbow room between them.

There were rare cases in which a desperately hard-pressed Casanova hired a boy to stroll by Maggie's house and lure the cat away. Some cats chased certain dogs, and certain cats chased other cats. Ever so infrequently, some barbarian would secrete a mouse in his coat pocket and turn it loose in the parlor. For his underhanded trouble he might get a fleeting hug from fear. A few exceedingly gallant but supremely naive boys gave their sweethearts canaries. But the canary was useless as highfaluting wedding china. All you could do was watch fatuously. You were afraid to approach either any nearer than five feet.

The swain's untarnished citadel, his exalted piece de resistance, was the horse. When wistfulness and wisteria were more pronounced, serious courting couples got a thousand miles of romancing in a ten mile ride in a buggy. The wretchedly zealous chaperone was left guarding a parlor shorn of love birds. Naturally, only couples who were practically engaged were permitted buggy privileges. However, if a chaperone had been insistently predatory, buggy seats were flagrantly narrow, nay, more, charmingly so. These buggy seats were so narrow it was said they were designed especially to carry two temperance workers. (Actually, this reference to bigotry was ascribed to a certain Protestant sect that will go nameless until interdenomination threats are made less seriously in small towns than at present.)

In the moonlight, the mystical moonshine of the pulsating night, Hubert and Maggie were transformed into Abelard and Heloise. The buggy was a Nicean barque or an opulent pumpkin on glistening wheels. Hubert dropped the reins on the splatter-board. Old Dobbin took so long to travel five miles the lovers ran the poignant gamut all the way from "The Sonnets from the Portuguese" to the "End of a Perfect Day."

Each 5280 feet there was a milepost that disclosed the distance to the town, but only incidentally. These mileposts were outdoor advertisements on whose lean, bare breasts were emblazoned the sagas of cheese, shoes, hip boots, kerosene oil, and Siedlitz powders. Or, this is what the mileposts revealed by sunlight. When the lovers passed in the buggy, the nitrate of soda advertisement was a valentine. There was a big heart and the words Hubert Entwhistle and Maggie Hotchkiss were written in gold, trimmed in silver, with a bleeding arrow quivering through the center.

Of course, the hayride gave the same impetus to wholesale matrimony that a war always does. The chaperone was mandatory on the hayride. And yet, the boys who made the arrangements were always wonderfully considerate and deferential to this lady detective. The chair was fixed with boards that looked like modern skis. These were nailed to the floor boards so the chair wouldn't jounce or topple the female Pinkerton. Incidentally, this chair was nailed to the back of the wagon, with the seat facing the dusty road behind.

Since the arrangers were inherently considerate, they never selected a lame or blind horse. Whenever feasible, they employed an asthmatic horse. The night air was so beneficial to respiratory troubles. The old wheezer had to stop every fifty yards for deep-breathing exercises, but if, perchance, one such creature went a hundred yards without pause, some kind-hearted young nobleman stopped the wagon to be sure the horse was all right.

There wasn't much smooching on the hayride. This was postponed until these hayride lovers' children got into parked cars. Too, the girls' laps were filled with platters of fried chicken and sandwiches. If you've never tried it, a bunch of soggy tomato sandwiches can impede the progress of love as much as an old-fashioned steering wheel. There was, have no doubt about it, a little footsie and coy hanky-panky in and under the hay—some toe caresses and some furtive pecks on the cheek and the back of the neck. If these lovers didn't get the full butt of the clip, maybe a sample opened more floodgates than a full bill of goods. But all the electricity of the night was not held in the elements of the sky. The small brush fires, the sharp but not lethal voltage culminated in large conflagrations. One hayriding couple made known its marital intentions and before you could roll a cigarette the local thrush was hunting extra copies of "The Sweetest Story Ever Told."

And, remember it or try to forget it, if you are old enough, the animal went to pre-nuptial celebrations, in many cases. A lot of small-town couples got milk cows for wedding presents. The reasoning was infallible: You could use expensive china and silverware but milk and butter you had to have if you wanted to live long to enjoy all the fruits of married love. Often, the cow was tied in the front yard, and she was pointed to and admired by the trilling conductresses who told all and sundry just what presents different folks had sent. (Readers of a former generation will remember such a wedding present being tied in the front yard of a United States Senator. This cow was photographed right along with the Dresden china and the Sheffield teapot.)

Of course, all this happened in a slowpoke era when there was no appalling hurry attached to buying a sack of popcorn or a cemetery plot. Everyone believed in ample and adequate preparation. Few big league managers sent pitchers into the ball game without warming them up properly. The same sort of procedure applied to the gentle art of courting and getting married.

The Twilight Owlets

It has already been recorded that the owl is a stupid stick-in-the-mud, a croaker of discordant gibberish, a mask of ugly and shiftless diffidence waiting for a hapless insect to deliver himself up as a welfare check.

The owlet, believe it or not, is almost as charming as the owl is ridiculously repulsive. Tragically the little screech owls grow up to be insolvent imbeciles. This same cruel transformation has happened before. (When Bluebeard was a little boy he had curls of yellow. He helped his mother regularly and sang in a boys' choir and learned his catechism, but, well, you know the story.)

When early summer weather is silky after supper, when the color curling from the woods is a sort of greenish blue, the owlets take off in the hit or miss way the Wrights did at Kitty Hawk. There is more of prayer than hope in these first flights. There is tremendous excitement among them but this excitement is all bound round with fear as the owlets flail, quiver, rise, and flounder onward at a slight altitude.

You like to believe the pull of youth and ambition kicks up the mischief of exploration in these owlets. They certainly put on a marvelous show, and the poet in you tries to push down the inevitable truth that these delightful twilight roisterers will finally hole up to become premature superannuates. But now the darkening woods hold a cargo of fragile delight and you return to your living room trying hard to keep from saying: Like father, like son. Too soon, O, much, much too soon.

Animals Have Vagaries, Too

In 1960, in Charleston, West Virginia, three horses smashed a Volkswagen. This could have been a simple accident, but these three horses may have remembered, suddenly, tales of their fathers and grandfathers being harassed or harmed by automobiles. Or this smashing of the Volkswagen could be a sympathetic gesture inspired by the ghastly news of the deportation of Irish horses for Belgian slaughter. Maybe, every dog in West Virginia has had his day already, and this singular occurrence was merely to call attention to the fact that horses still exist.

There's always the possibility the three horses smelled glue. Or, it could be these are ultra provincials, militant defenders of the status that hate any kind of foreign competition. Of course, these horses may have recalled their distant cousin, the celebrated blind mule, that really wasn't blind but was supremely indifferent to what and whom he ran against.

Animals are not always servile. For instance, several years ago some foxes in Granville County, N. C., are said to have kidnaped a big Walker hound. Unfortunately no eyewitnesses remain. Many folks have heard of the wondrous talking crow that lived in Habersham County, Ga., that could do long division. The crow's master ran a country store and the bird did most of the bookkeeping. The crow eventually went on an utter silence strike after saying to his employer: "Buy yourself a damned adding machine."

In the Dismal Swamp there was the medically minded bear that preached vigorously against honey and the possible consequences of diabetes. And almost everyone knows of the mule in South Carolina that invaded a polling place. Some folks believed this mule thought he was a donkey and entitled to vote, but many others said he just smelled a bale of hay. You can't ever tell what a horse is thinking. There is the well known story of the horse trainer in Virginia who tried to pacify a restive steed by explaining: "After all, Sir Reginald, men and horses are pretty much alike." The horse shook his head and replied: "Maybe, but you put cream and sugar on your shredded wheat."

Two or three years ago, at the Ware County, Ga., prison camp, the bloodhounds tunneled under the wire of the compound and vanished into the countryside. (This is true as the story about the Charleston horses.) The inmates, the convicts, were assembled and pressed into service to recapture the bloodhounds. Sending a convict to capture a bloodhound is worse than asking the President of Eastern Air Lines to make an eloquent speech requesting the return of the Pony Express. By comparison, asking the regent of the UDC to eulogize Sherman is no task at all.

Duty, as General Lee said, may be the sublimest word in the language. Even so there is a limit to which no leash can be pulled. If anyone in this nation has ever been pardoned for saying, "I just ain't going to do it, damn it all," then these hapless wretches in the Georgia prison camp ought to be inexorably absolved. The tragedy of this story is that it could not have anything approaching a happy or satisfactory ending. There was

no bounty, trophy, or brush awarded. No sentence was short-
ened, even by parenthesis. The only reward was mosquitoes,
chiggers, face-whipping with branches, spills from undergrowth,
hunger, and thirst.

And a buck will get you ten the next time a convict goes
under the wire, the fool bloodhounds will forget how they were
rescued from the perils of the hinterlands. Yes, sir, those wicked
ingrates will take out after the convict boy as if he were a piece
of elusive, red meat. Mark Twain said if you feed a hungry
dog and make him prosperous he will not bite you, and that,
he said, is the principal difference between a dog and a man.
But Mark Twain was talking about city dogs that have been
exposed to Salvation Army workers and street corner services.
There are a lot of bloodhounds at Georgia prison camps that
never wear roses on Mother's Day, bathe only every other Saturday, and have not repaid one single cent they ever snitched
from the mite box.

Again the true revelation: Farmers in Coon Valley, Wiscon-
sin, waited interminably for federal action on an application
for a flood control program. Promises were long and frequent
but action was thinner than the flap on a match packet. While
this application was still tied up in the thicket of hogwash,
some beavers constructed four separate dams and solved the
flood control problem.

This happened in 1958 and you can look it up.

Maybe these beavers read the Congressional Record. Perhaps,
the action was purely in self-interest but there is a possibility the
altruistic sensibilities of the beavers were touched by the plight
of the Coon Valley farmers. Then, again, the four dams may
have been a go-to-hell gesture directed at the coons for whom
the valley is named.

The coon is aloof as a Ku Kluxer at a Harlem night club.

Anti-social, fractious, and mumbling under his bottom lip, the coon harbors no pleasantry even for the thoughtful people who call a precinct after him. Drenched in grumpy austerity he sits atop a high tree and lets the land below go to watery wrack. So, these beavers may have waited for the right opportunity to try to teach the coon a graphic lesson in community responsibility. But for all anyone knows, the peevish coon may have reported the beavers for building dams without legal permits; for using material not up to government specification; for failure to procure proper condemnations; for failure to comply with the articles of Eminent Domain; and surely, if nothing else, for neglecting to provide recreational parks and eating stands along public right-of-ways.

In fact, these beavers may be prosecuted for academic deficiencies. You have to have a degree from a four year engineering school to build dams. Also, there are bound to be laxities in wages and hours, especially in overtime. Since beavers can't eat the standard prison diet, since penologists eschew preferential foods, these beavers may be waiting to take joy rides at Cape Canaveral.

Mr. Pussy

This is a tale I've heard told in Oxford, N. C., a thousand times. Frankly, I can't vouch for the authenticity. Some of the people who told this tale were, as they say, straight along and all right from the ground up. Some others who swore by this tale also swore the world was flat, or, otherwise, eggs would fall out of the nest during the night. Some others were Sunday School teachers and still others voted three times for William Jennings Bryan and I don't mean in three different Presidential elections.

Mr. Pussy was a drummer. His card introduced him as a "Rodent Exterminator." Despite the specious asininity of the business card, the word trickled around from county to county that Mr. Pussy was a cracker-jack rat-killer. Mr. Pussy, it is told, wore the dark suits and string ties of the era. He wore an enormous black hat and a ruffled white shirt. He had a black moustache and long sideburns.

Sometimes, when I have heard Mr. Pussy described, I have thought of Edgar Allen Poe. At other descriptions, I have thought of Paladin, the soft-talking gun-slinger on television. Maybe, this is because of the card he handed around. Mr. Pussy came to town alone. The other drummers traveled together, normally. They rode the same train so they could chip in on a hired hack to make their rounds to the rural stores, after they had called on the merchants in the county seats.

The other drummers carried flat sample cases. Mr. Pussy's sample case was a big box, a sort of hatbox contraption with a few holes bored in the top. If there was an uncontrollable epidemic of rats in a community, he took his card and the hat-box to the town commissioners. Usually, though, he called on merchants, or perhaps large farmers, whose stores or crops were being badly damaged by rats. He would offer to do an exterminating job at so much per rat head, or he would guarantee to clean out a store or big corn crib at a flat rate.

Mr. Pussy carried in his inside coat pocket a newspaper clipping that told how he had wiped out the rats in an entire country, some little country in South, Latin, or Central America. The king or emperor or whatever kind of ruler the country had, gave him a gold medal. This gold medal had a Latin inscription, or it may have been Spanish. The local Sunday school teachers said it was Latin, that the medal came free at the Philadelphia centennial of 1876. The three-time losers, the Bryan voters, said No, by God, it was Spanish and the ruler down yonder had it made specially for Mr. Pussy.

(The straight along and all right people said you could have these clippings made up in a print shop. The flat-worlders knew this was an infernal lie. They said, Oh, yea, Unca Sam would put your Francis in Atlanta for counterfeiting.)

Because of the nature of his work, Mr. Pussy didn't keep to a regular schedule such as was adhered to by the drummers who sold lamp chimneys or rubber boots. No, you'd look up one day and he'd be standing in front of the Confederate Monument. He rolled his cigarettes with one hand, against the breeze, and he must have been a shattering resemblance to the gun-fighter as he stood there in the shadow of the monument to the dead, twirling his big hat-box the same paralyzing way a hired gun fingers his holster.

Then like an especially consecrated hawk to its prey, he'd swoop down on the place in which he had business. There were two samples in his drummer's case, in the huge hat-box. Both had collars and tiny chains. When one was put on the showcase or counter, all the customers and loafers broke for the sidewalk. Sample Number 1 was Goliath, a big yellow tom-cat with whiskers as sharp and sturdy as well-honed nails. Goliath reared on his hind legs, smote his broad chest with his front paws. He was the lethal quintessence of a yellow King Kong. Instead of purring, Goliath rasped the way giant chains rattle, the way a hurricane rasps and snorts.

Lucretia, the other sample, was blacker than all the pits and starless nights combined. She was small, and according to all the old timers, Bryans and straight alongers, she could do three back flips without touching ground. It was said she had been trained for her profession on flying squirrels. She was fast and deadly as a snake. She would draw into a black ball no bigger than a baby's mitten. Then she'd strike with the straight swiftness of an arrow.

There you have the picture, Goliath, the broadsword, Lucretia, the dagger up the coat sleeve. One was a brute and the other a serpent and each was deadly as sin in the first phase of New England.

It has been told that Mr. Pussy never fed these samples. No, indeed. No work, no rations. (Somebody told me, I remembered it this minute, Mr. Pussy watered the samples on a compound of whiskey and vinegar, laced with specks of bole pepper. There may be something to that; everybody knows you have to water a cat or it will die in three days.)

After the crowd had quieted, Mr. Pussy would take a rat from one of his black pockets. If he was sampling Goliath, he would throw the rat as far as he could. Goliath would spring from the showcase, plowing straight ahead with all the force of a Coast Guard Cutter. A chair meant nothing to Goliath. He hit it, knocked it to one side, and stormed ahead without breaking his prodigious stride.

If Mr. Pussy was sampling Lucretia, he would toss the rat as high as the ceiling. Often he would go outside and toss the rat as if he were knocking out a fly ball. Lucretia erupted angrily as the meanest geyser. Frequently, she caught the rat before it had a chance to start falling. (I've heard old-timers say Lucretia had the amazing grace of Hal Chase. Others compared her to Tris Speaker in the Grey Eagle's great hours, when he outran fly balls, caught them in his hip pocket, as they say.)

After the sampling exhibitions, Mr. Pussy would get down to business terms. As a rule, because he had several states to cover, he took an order for one Goliath or one Lucretia, or so many of each, with, naturally, a three per cent discount for cash for so many in the shipping barrel.

If, however, typhus was believed imminent, he did the job while he was in town. The fee was larger for the personal extermination. Not only did the local customer have the benefit of Mr. Pussy's supervision but it is said, too, his long experience enabled him to smell a rat better than a temperance sister could smell booze. They say, they all agree, Mr. Pussy's smelling genius worked even when he had a heavy cold in the head.

Now, it so happened, during Garfield's Administration, Mr. Pussy was called to Oxford, by telegram, mind you, for an emergency. The rats had taken over the largest grocery store in town. Customers were afraid to walk on that side of the street, much less to enter the store. But as luck would have it, the store burned to the ground the night before Mr. Pussy and Goliath and Lucretia got to Oxford. The store rats took the hint and left town. It is generally accepted that the rats thought malicious arson had occurred just for their diabolical benefit. This was not the case, as was legally established when the merchant sued the fire insurance company.

Well, Mr. Pussy was mad as if someone had sent him a rubber mouse on Christmas day. Still and all, no extermination, no cake, is the way of it sometimes. Mr. Pussy stomped around town for a day or two, cussing kerosene lamps and faulty flues and hick towns that favor horse troughs over hydrants. That Oxford was in a small recession is typified by the shocking paucity of sales of traps and cheese.

Just as Mr. Pussy was about to leave town, for good and all, an old man from Sassafras Fork Township came hunting him. This old man, Mr. Tarapin-Eye Tulgin, located Mr. Pussy in the bar room in Oxford. They had a drink or two and talked about tricks in general for a while. Then Mr. Tarapin-Eye

Tulgin said he had a proposition to make Mr. Pussy. Mr. Tarapin smiled sort of foolishly and said he reckoned Goliath and Lucretia could kill most any kind of rat. Show, show, he was show of that, but Mr. Pussy brought out his Spanish medal and vowed that in a reasonable time, Goliath and Lucretia could kill all the rats in the world.

Mr. Tarapin-Eye Tulgin joshed along. He turned the conversation to gambling. He let on that gambling was his one fatal fault. Yes sir, he told how he had lost the best plantation in the county trying to catch an inside straight, how he had lost the second best plantation in the county the time he caught the inside straight. While they stood there at the bar, Mr. Tarapin-Eye Tulgin made two or three half-witted bets for small amounts, drinks and fifty cents and so on. Mr. Pussy probably thought the old man was crazy, but the store having burned and all, he was glad for the chance at a little change and some free drinks.

By and by, Mr. Tarapin-Eye Tulgin said how would Mr. Pussy take to this proposition: He had several corn cribs and cotton houses and a big stable that hadn't room for anything but the rats that were in them. Mr. Tarapin-Eye said he knew he was doing a drunken thing but he had a pet rat, a sort of heirloom, he'd put up in a fist-and-skull, no-holds-barred, head-to-head fight with either one of Mr. Pussy's samples.

Quick as Lucretia in orbit, Mr. Pussy whipped out some paper and wrote down the terms of the bet. He wrote so fast he broke his pencil twice. He wanted it down before this old goat got sober and came to his senses, if he had any. The bartender and a pool hustler witnessed the contract. The contract stipulated that if Mr. Tarapin-Eye Tulgin's rat whipped one sample, the other sample would exterminate all the pests free of charge.

If the sample won, Mr. Tarapin-Eye would pay $100.00 flat rate or a nickel a head, whichever was the greater sum.

Mr. Pussy ran to the depot and got his hatbox and he and Mr. Tarapin-Eye got into the buggy and headed for the Tulgin place. The arena was a pit used ordinarily for cock fighting.

As gloomy as Mr. Pussy was, he almost busted his ruffled shirt-waist trying to keep from laughing out loud. He almost had a convulsion when Mr. Tarapin-Eye brought out this rat about as big as a two-day old bitty. It had a beard to its toes, a floppy ear, and cataracts over both eyes.

Of course, Mr. Pussy wanted to know the joke. What kind of damned hotel bill is this anyhow, he thundered. Who ever heard of anything so preposterous. The very idea. Imagine, just imagine, putting one of his samples against a rat that was waiting at Roanoke Island when the settlers arrived.

Old man Tarapin-Eye, he laughed too, and pulled down a jug and they drank a little bit more, and then, he said, shucks, they'd come out here, so they might as well have the fight, anyhow. Mr. Pussy replied with some sarcastic cuss words as he lifted Lucretia from the hat-box and snapped off the chain. You could tell the sample thought Mr. Pussy was drunk, but, shaking her head, she vaulted onto the piece of meat. She toyed with the rat for a second or two, for sport. Mr. Pussy snapped his fingers and she snarled and made a ferocious pass, one of such agility as to compliment a ballet dancer. The rat turned a forward somersault, bounced up behind Lucretia, crawled along her heaving back, and whispered in her ear.

Lucretia waddled over to a corner of the pit, sat down and crossed her legs and whimpered for some milk. Mr. Tarapin-Eye picked up a milk bucket, but before he could reach the cow in the stall, Mr. Pussy killed Lucretia with a pitchfork.

Mr. Tarapin-Eye flung a bandana to the rat and he dabbed at his cataracts. Mr. Pussy yanked that tremendous Goliath from the hat-box with such force he almost broke the chain in two. He kicked Goliath in the rear and, for the first time in his life, raised his voice and screamed: Kill that Goddam rat and be quick about it. Goliath went across the pit faster than old engine 97 coming down the fatal grade. The furious yellow sample hit the side of the pit so hard the echo kicked up dust back in Oxford. But he was up in a flash, on his hind legs, roaring wildly as a lion with a splinter in his paw.

Just as Goliath was about to strike, the rat ran up his stomach and started doing a miniature buck and wing. Old Goliath toppled over backwards and laughed himself to death. (There was some type of hemorrhage, due, no doubt, to the paroxysm of laughing. Albeit, the coroner's certificate is not recorded, if, indeed, there ever was one.)

Mr. Pussy walked back to town, throwing the hat-box in the river on the way. For months he walked blindly, perpetually in a trance. He was a fruit jar of whiskey turned to talcum water, an anvil turned to jello. Without fire or purpose he stumbled around Oxford, always groping in shadows of inner darkness. During a storm, even a small one, he crawled under a store. The only time he ever gritted his teeth was when some kind-hearted person would let him drown an ailing cat.

If he saw a rat trap he shook so violently he had to be given morphine. He had not the wit nor will to seek alms. Compassionate people left trays at the back doors for Mr. Pussy. Eventually, he turned more and more to booze and he died one day in an agonizing delirium, screaming that rats were gnawing on his innards.

Now, do you want to know what the rat said to Lucretia?

Old man Tarapin-Eye just grinned and said if you can't whip 'em fair and square, why kill 'em with flattery or tickle 'em to death. Actually, all sides agree he did say this rat was the very same one whose niece was courted by the froggie. Remember the song:

> "Froggie went a-courting and he did ride,
> Sword and pistol by his side, Um-huh.
> He rode up to Miss Mousy's house,
> Asked Miss Mousy for to be his spouse, Um-huh.
> —Not without Uncle Rat's consent,
> Would I marry the President, Um-huh, Um-huh."

All sides, flat-worlders and straight alongers, knew this was a contemptible lie. Old man Tarapin-Eye was denounced as a blatherskite. Can you imagine anyone with the unmitigated temerity to try to pass as gospel the nutty story that a rat in a folk song was a real rat after all. And that nonsense about a froggie trying to marry a mouse. That's the trouble with those old-timey story tellers. They could stick strickly to the truth for eight innings but they'd louse it up in the last stanza, just as surely as Mr. Pussy made a tragic mistake when he didn't get right back on the train when he learned the store had burned down the night before.

Scare-Crow in Autumn

The scare-crow that remains when the crop is gone is a soldier doing guard duty whom the brass forgot to tell about the war's being over. He's all dressed-up in his ridiculous hand-me-down finery with absolutely no place to go. He reminds you of a rusty tool left standing in the rain. Unlike the man in the old song, the scare-crow not only had a hat when he came out last Spring but he's still got one in Fall. But this chapeau isn't worth stealing. No hunter has taken it for pathetic sport nor any hobo for battered usefulness. It was also eschewed by the woodpecker who bored holes in the scare-crow's ears for trinkets he will never wear.

The scare-crow, vigilantly protecting barren acres, shakes all spectators with laughter, with merriment that approaches the ribald. And yet to the sentimentalist the scare-crow is a forsaken old man who is patiently waiting for a gala parade that passed and left the county a month ago. The impotent specter is futile as the silly mistakes you made in your childhood and can never correct.

The scare-crow is a dreary stick in a musty museum, but he does have one vital function. He is to the wise crow what a static, insoluble issue is to a political candidate,—an eruption of manna, a fountain of merciful hope and intervention. The wise crow, the peerless leader, spares his vocal chords during winter's waste, but when the scare-crow mounts his battlements in Spring, the matchless ramrod is Daniel Webster with his britches filled with hornets. The scare-crow has no more pertinence to the year's corn crop than Dixie freight rates have to lunar explorations. Yet, by dint of the matchless leader's purple rhetoric, the hapless drudge, the scare-crow, becomes such a dread apparition you'd think a famine is imminent. Since the advent of compulsory education, many crows know the stick sentinel is as vacuous as the promise of the old-time Southern bellwether to make the trains run on time. But when the leader of the flock unleashes his blistering denunciation, his constituents act as if the plan of feathery salvation is reduced to a quick summary.

It's peculiar. The average crow understands the man on the battlements hasn't frightened anyone out of a single roasting-ear since Cole Blease was a barefoot boy. But just let fury fly from the leader's graveled cornets and the constituents see the sum of all earthly opposition reduced to the bedraggled stumble-bum, to the ludicrous guard who is sans arms and armament.

The magpie flies the way poets sing, and the mockingbird pours honey on the residual wounds of winter. But when the peerless leader's band plays "Way Down Yonder in the Corn Field" all the constituents chant wildly as the nuthatch and the flapping of many small wings is the thunder of the eagle's plunge.

To leave politics where they belong, you know that old man winter will strip the scare-crow bare and bury his blackened, wooden carcass beneath the seasonal avalanches. Before the day of interment, some irate and luckless quail hunter will shoot the sentinel in the back, but the lone hound improvising a rabbit hunt will not even trouble to give him the time of day. The scare-crow, the tragic comedian, stands against the toppling darkness of late Fall as a hump-backed, immobile Don Quixote, shorn even of a windmill to pursue.

Good-bye, Brer Mule

"Johnson had an old gray mule,
 He drove him to a cart;
 John loved the mule, and the mule loved John
 With all his mulish heart.
 The rooster crowed and Johnson knowed
 That day was bout to break;
 So, he curried mule with a three-legged stool
 And wiped him off with a rake."

To a disheartening and shocking degree that old, old song is typical of the saga of the mule. Figuratively or actually, most of us have returned Brer Mule's devotion and dedication to labor much in the manner of Johnson. The piano part of the ancient ditty is so obvious it may be elusive: Johnson really loved his mule but Johnson seemed to think the mule thought hard physical knocks to be the only sensible manner of demonstrating affection.

Old man mule is the proper symbol for enduring tragedy. This shamefully maligned creature enters the world as a bastard, an Ishmaelite denied the succor of ancestry and the inspiration of posterity. There is in his eyes an incomparable sadness. This look, this gallant sort of pitifulness, must be predicated on the mule's awareness that he can't produce any progeny. And yet, the individual mule, and mule as a symbol of a way of life, require a lot of repeated killing. If wanton neglect and continued abuse were lethal, the mule would have been dead long ago.

There may be some diabolical nuance of some science that will replace and displace us all. But old man mule has seen his harness bend and break in his own time. On countless farms the hoary harness room is a playground for mice and spider webs.

104

It is an evil contest between the two to determine which one will preempt the place first. The wind rattles the raw innards and bones of the old room and a detached sort of leukemia works from the roof downwards. On wall pegs molding mule collars form rancid zeros through which the luscious greenery of buried Junes has paraded to oblivion.

It is dismaying enough to see your own hallowed bailiwick usurped by a younger, more virile version of yourself. But to see himself run from the field by an iron monster must be almost more than even Brer Mule's long and stolid sufferance can stand. Yet, the mule carries on the ancient symbol even amid the clattering din of ten billion kinds of tractors and farm machinery.

Even so, it is difficult to remember that a few mules are still led out each morning when the earth is soft and sweet, when spring lays her golden eggs and decorates her woodlands with sticks of striped candy. A few die-hard farmers are royally impervious to these "confletched" motorized contraptions. A few farmers, not only born to, but in the land, have been bound round with mules so long that the breaking of land in any other way would be a small sacrilege. The mule and the plow, going straight ahead, even as dynasties topple, is a type of secular religion. As was the case with Johnson in the song, some farmers have cussed a pet mule so many years the scathing epithets now blend into and form an unpublished volume of rustic poetry, an anthology of ribald humor. In fact, there have been farmers who were so sick they had to lean against the fence to cough. But they could still cuss the mule.

Old man mule is the butt of ten million flippant jokes. People who never touched a live mule have used him as illustration for arrant perversity. Again, stupid people have been compared stupidly to mules by other stupid people. The noble horse,

contrariwise, has been lionized, patronized, and all but canon-
ized. Poets still fly amid slushy eloquence to testify to the horse's
intelligence, fidelity, and stamina. "Horse-sense" is an intellec-
tual accolade in the missile era.

Nonetheless, any competent authority will explain that the
horse is merely the fortunate and accidental beneficiary of the
mule's stolen honors. Under pressure, a horse is nervous and
fractious as a high-wire walker in a terrific lightning storm. If a
horse catches his foot in a fence he will cut it frightfully in his
violent anguish. The docile mule will stand quietly and wait
patiently for a man to extricate the foot.

An over-heated horse will kill himself drinking, if not
arrested. If he is ravenously hungry, he will kill himself eating,
if not stopped. On the other hand the thirsty or starving mule
will eat and drink just enough to satisfy his actual needs. If you
over-load a wagon, the tempestuous horse will break into a fear-
ful lather trying with tremulous and foolish desperation, to
move the load. Under the same conditions, the mule will pull,
then tug hard, figure out the load is too heavy, and then will
stand with unaffected nonchalance until some of the weight is
removed.

(Farmers are fond of an old saying that goes: "Whoever saw
a dead mule?" Translated, this means that cemeteries and medical hospitals, bone-yards and veterinarians' quarters are filled
with men and animals who broke all the rules of health and diet
to which the mule clings so tenaciously. The phrase, "Whoever
saw a dead mule?" is a reluctant tribute but is opprobrious,
simultaneously, because it is spoken with poorly concealed rancor. The implication is that a mule has no moral right to per-
sonify the tenets of health which are so recklessly violated by
men.)

There are a billion paintings, posters, photographs, and pieces of sculpture of the noble horse. Only the democrats and a plug of chewing tobacco have bothered with Brer Mule. And yet, this offspring of the male ass and mare, the common mule, is mentioned in the Holy Writ and in Greek and Latin literature. The trouble is the mule has had isolated men who loved him but cussed him, whereas the horse has had more publicity agents than all the stars in Hollywood's history. For instance, the legendary warriors and generals are shown with their faithful and heroic steeds. (Only a few years ago every school child had to memorize Thomas B. Reed's poem about the horse that carried General Sheridan to Winchester to save the day for the Federal Army. Although the poet, Reed, didn't say so positively, the reader gets the unalterable impression that the Yankee soldiers, rifles, and cannons were superfluous baggage. The horse got top billing in the drama and General Sheridan was the male lead.)

Before motorized warfare, including World War I, the long-suffering mule was used as pack and draught animal. Apparently nerveless, he stood during the searing barrages as if hitched to the plow. As an ammunition carrier, old man mule was led to the worst of the fighting a billion times. When this same experiment was tried with the horse it was usually found the horse was as dangerous as the enemy.

The courage and remarkable equipoise of Brer Mule may be due to his uncanny ability to protect himself, almost effortlessly, during dangerous conditions. As is the nimblest, natural-born athlete, the mule is endowed with the capacity to roll with all punches. This rolling with the punches is second nature and is done without deliberation.

To use the horse again as illustration: Barrels of glue could be made from the horses that have broken legs fleeing from thunderstorms. The mule seems to know the storm will pass, no matter how intensely it beats. When the heavens seem to go temporarily insane with flashing mayhem, the mule looks upward calmly as if to say: "Well, what else is news today?"

No matter, though, we are bound to be speaking in the past tense, even despite the few farmers who are so wedded to the symbol of earth and plow that any kind of tractor is a freak from outer space. The mule and all he represents in a way of life is long ago and shoved away. The mule represents the vanquished hours of complacent insularity. The mule is the epitome of that shaded, provincial, unhurried, gregarious era when the Tar Heel farmer thought Arizona as exotic and as bizarre as his son thinks the space beyond the moon is today.

The mule is irrevocably and nostalgically tied in with the baseball game at the cross-roads, with the local fiddlers' contest, with the "sociable" at the schoolhouse, the corn shucking, the house-warming, and the great August revival meeting. And always beyond the symbol and the usages of metaphor, the mule meant bread. If the corn field was bread in the shucks, the mule was the only road to that field. With the passing of old man mule, a flaring industry has gone with the son of the wind that wrecked Margaret Mitchell's feudal realm. Just yesterday, Brer Mule was big business, and not merely comparably so. Bread and meat and education and tombstones rode on his back.

The mule was to the economy of ten thousand dusty Southern towns what sex is to Hollywood and to the slick magazines. His honking-yonking and his hee-hawing, that sprightly gesture of supreme indifference, were inseparable from the hopes of a people. The mule market was not only big business but its demise has stolen from our midst a zizzling profession. The mule trader, with his plug hat, jaunty apparel, and flashing cane (the cane was his trade-mark), could talk faster and much more

perceptively than a tobacco auctioneer. Despite his rapid and
clearly audible chatter, he was as elusive as a gnat in an empty
subway tunnel. Double-talk was for beginners. This man would
be describing the incredible merits of the Tennessee mule hal-
tered at hand, but before you could light a cigarette he would
run around the world in verbal jet excursions. If you weren't
careful he had sold you a slouchy mule but you somehow got
the peculiar impression he had thrown in a couple of the pyra-
mids and a Parisian can-can dancer. You could bust an anvil
easier than you could fatigue one of his mules, just slightly.
Why, he had swum one of his weaker mules clean through the
Johnstown Flood. Last week, just last week, he sold the governor
two prime beauties. And what was more, he knew straight from
the governor's mouth what was trumps in hearts and spades.

Most all the local "time" stores sold mules. There was a stable
behind the big store. There was a regular procession in and out
of the stable. These spontaneous tours by prospective owners
and the merely curious were conducted by a "time" store salesman who devoted all his energies to selling mules. He was a
double first cousin of the professional from afar. He could talk
almost as rapidly as the pro with the stick. He was almost as
adroit with the double-entendre but, of course, he couldn't palm
off the fabulous travelogues of the wizard from afar. (Afar often
indicated no distance greater than the next state, if, indeed,
some place more than two counties away.)

Although mules were standard stocks of goods, the same as
kerosene oil and bolts of calico, special emphasis came during
the quarterly sessions of the county court. Everybody but the
totally blind and the completely halt came to town. The room-
ing houses put in trundle beds, cots, and pallets and even at
that the waves of humanity spilled onto the porches and lawns.
In fair weather, people slept in and under wagons. The court-

house was the one shining hub encased in a golden magnet. The drama and excitement of the court room drew the crowds. In a week's time there was everything from a Greek tragedy to the enactment of a tale that could have been written by Augustus Baldwin Longstreet or Bret Harte. Justice was grim and unadorned as barbed wire. It was as gullible as the sucker who bought the Brooklyn Bridge. It was awesome and inspiring as a Confederate parade. It was as outrageously funny and as badly disordered as a Mack Sennett comedy.

The 24 ring dramatic carnival upstairs in the court room fetched the thirsty and hungry pilgrims. This having been accomplished, every conceivable type of huckster and two-bit con man was ready with his wares. Two or three mule sales went on at the same time. During court week swapping came to the fore rather more than straight sales. The man who wouldn't steal a coal of fire from the devil delighted in sticking the mule trader. The mule trader was fair game for every ruse and artifice. It was always open season on him, with no bag limit. However, the experienced traders always got back a little bit better than they gave. There was, however, the story in every community about the novice who was given a mule one day during court week and told to trade as many different times as he possibly could in one day. This was to give the novice experience. At sundown the novice ended up with a broken pocket-knife and half a plug of chewing tobacco but no mule.

Some farmers went home from court week with spavined mules, blind ones, and some so old and feeble they must have been on the boat ride with Noah. But getting stuck with a lot of mulish imperfections wasn't so onerous as being victimized by other frauds. No. The farmer usually laughed and said that he might not have much of a mule but even a piece of mule was like a small amount of whiskey. It might not go far but you couldn't beat it for the distance it went.

Perhaps, it is patently silly to argue too much for the mule way and to argue too much against the tractor way. But the night the "Old Nostalgia" burned down there were no mules inside. The truth is that Brer Mule has about shot his wad and there is hardly a barnyard rooster to crow him a requiem. Perhaps, the true ending of the saga occurred in the spring of 1960 when a tenant farmer in Sampson County, N. C., drowned himself because his mule died.

The mule had belonged to the man for 18 years. A death note said simply: "My old mule is dead and I want to die now too." It is hard to resist the temptation to dramatize the unspeakable pathos attendant upon primitive man and his mule. Obviously this man and his mule worked in double harness, physically and spiritually, so to say. (This Sampson County relationship is true but it is used to represent thousands of similar associations, save for the suicide, of course.)

They toiled in the same steaming fields, saw the same sunsets, were exposed to the same weather and seasonal caprices, and they were both awake and asleep comparable amounts of time. They both ate humble fare and slept in cheerless places. The world and all its mystery and enchantment was bounded by the last rows of the fields they plowed. If either's ambition was ever quickened by the rising sun, long hours of unrequited attrition preempted such tender hopefulness and left in its stead only the hunger pangs of late morning or the blessed respite of a shade tree amid July's devastating brimstone.

But as persistently as the aching dramatic portrait pulls at heart and mind, there is a deeper, broader consideration. As a type this man in Sampson County is of a tribe whose sole objective is physical survival. In the light of current scientific knowledge, of expanding comforts, of rapidly accruing social benefits, it is difficult for the uninitiated to understand that there are still living countless men whose entire program of daily salvation is reduced to getting through an hour, to conquering a week by sheer, unvarnished, blind diligence, to outlasting a year by fortune and main strength and awkwardness.

A good year is a period relatively free from pain and anguish. A good year is one in which there are no large disasters. For the unbalance between a crop made and the tangible results of a harvest is a form of mathematical wizardry too intricate for mere mortals. Often life itself is sustained by the nebulous intimations of the ancient petition, "Next year with any luck I'll pay the time merchant, the landlord, and the bank and have something left over." But it may turn out that "next year" is the one hurdle physical endurance doesn't have the will to try to surmount.

This dead mule represented security. In the man's mind the mule was sustenance as well as affection. The man could get another mule, perhaps, but he had no desire to assist time's morbid continuation when the mule died. The fortunes of some men and their mules are so inextricably woven it would seem decent and proper to bury both in the same grave.

The Sampson County case is a rarity, but it will suffice for the saga of the mule. So wave to Brer Mule tenderly, you have known the pang of a stumped toe or the rapture of the first wild raspberries. Hunt down one vociferous rooster and have him crow the doxology for Brer Mule, and for a way of life, and all that and all that. The tractor has curried Brer Mule with its caterpillar treads and dug his grave with an iron spoon.